The Spiritual Writings of B.J. Palmer

The Second Chiropractor
volume 1

by Simon A. Senzon, M.A., D.C.

Bliss
226 Elk Avenue
P.O. Box # 2330
Crested Butte, CO 81224

Published by Simon A. Senzon
Asheville, North Carolina

.

The Spiritual Writings of B.J. Palmer
The Second Chiropractor
volume 1

Third Edition.
All rights reserved.
Copyright © 2004 by Simon A. Senzon.

This book or its parts may not be reproduced or copied by any means
with the exception of brief quotations for review or reference purposes,
without the written permission of the author.

Printed in the U.S. by Instantpublisher.com

A percentage of the author's proceeds from this book will be donated
for Chiropractic research.

*All quotations by B.J. Palmer as well as photos are used with the
permission of Palmer College of Chiropractic and the Palmer College
Archives.*

Acknowledgements

The author would like to thank Rob Sinnott for his efforts in compiling
the green books onto a useable format. I would also like to thank the
following people for inspiration, encouragement, and support; Ken
Wilber, Allan Combs, Ralph Boone, Brian McAulay, Dan Lemberger,
Donald Epstein, Susann Cooke-Greuter, Renee Graziano, Mike
Johnson, John Claussen, Lauren Lawson, Aaron Cloutier, Michael
Cotton, Reggie Tidwell, Lonnie Lapore, my parents, Ivan and Roni
Senzon, and countless other friends and family. Also, a special thank
you to Susan, my wife, without whom this project could never have
happened.

Requests for copies of this book should be made to:
www.PhilosophyOfChiropractic.com

Contents

Preface

The following quotations were written by B.J. Palmer (1881-1961), by his own account, the second chiropractor. These writings represent a distinct period of his life, from 1949-1961. During that time Palmer published fifteen books totaling 8045 pages.

The emphasis of this text is on Palmer's "spiritual writings." Thus, anything that relates to either his spirituality, or extends from his direct spiritual insights into other topics such as chiropractic, vertebral subluxation, religion, enlightenment, death, and divinity is included when appropriate.

Chiropractors in every spectrum of the profession, from non-therapeutic subluxation centered to therapeutic physicians have sought to distance the profession from its past and these writings in particular. This is a mistake.

Palmer's writings represent a very unique perspective in the history of health and healing in America. Not only does he discuss the healing process and the role of the body's internal wisdom in health, well-being, quality of life, spirituality, and religion; but he speaks directly to the current trends in the culture. In many regards, he was an early proponent of an integral approach to healing.

B.J. Palmer was far ahead of his time. Many in the profession have not taken the time to truly study his later works. One of the reasons for this was that B.J. had a very abrasive style of communication. As he built the chiropractic profession, he polarized large segments of his base. This has lead to a mythologizing of who he was and what his role was. Many chiropractic students today and probably most chiropractors have no idea that B.J. wrote anything about spirituality!

If the chiropractors have not read Dr. Palmer, you can bet that most health professionals be they M.D., acupuncturist, massage therapist, naturopath, or homeopath have not read him either. This is due to several reasons;

1) Palmer's writings were never widely distributed outside of the chiropractic profession,

2) Palmer's writings are quite difficult to study (future scholars may determine his grammatical and didactic style to be of a certain peculiar type),

3) As mentioned above, most of the profession has purposefully distanced the public and other health professionals away from Palmer's writings.

There is a very large segment of the chiropractic profession that embrace B.J. Palmer as an inspiration and a founding father. It is these chiropractors that I expect will be the first to realize the importance of this book. (Please, to those of you who have read B.J., do not expect to find your favorite quotes.)

I have excerpted and cut passages freely from these fifteen books in the hopes of making the material easier to study. A passage that has been cut will be represented by three periods, "...." Unusual spelling, capitalization, and other highlights have been preserved from the original writings. There are several passages that are extensive. To cut them would have lost too much of their essence.

I have laid out the topics chronologically when possible. I have also organized the main themes into several sections. These are designed to flow one into the other, and build on each other. In fact, I have determined two periods of Palmer's later writings; one from 1949-1953 and the other form 1955-1961. The topics from the first are titled "book one" and are clustered around the first period. The topics from "book two" are clustered around the second period. When topics were the same or very similar, I have mixed these two periods.

The book is meant to be a source of inspiration. I recommend for the first reading that the reader start at the beginning. This is by no means necessary. I have chosen each quote so that they will stand on their own. In that regard the book can be opened at random. Some of the passages might need to be read several times for the profound insights to become clear.

If there are better quotes that I have missed for certain topics, I beg the reader's indulgence. I have chosen what I think to be the crest jewels of the "Green Books."

I present this material with no apologies. B.J. Palmer was at times prophetic, and sometimes abrasive. His insights, although written fifty years ago, will be revolutionary for many people.

This volume shows a consistency in his spiritual writings that have never been presented in such a fashion. My hope is that the reader will enjoy them as I have.

These writings have a life of their own. Taken together in this fashion, they form a book that can be studied and used as an instruction manual. Call it B.J.'s instructions for health, success, and happiness, or Chiropractic meditations on awakening.

Perhaps it has taken so long for the world to embrace these teachings because it just wasn't ready yet.

This first volume is being presented without much commentary. A future volume will contain extensive commentary and supporting chapters. Enjoy.

Simon A. Senzon, M.A., D.C.   August, 2003

B.J. 1910   ·   B.J. 1960

Giant vs. Pygmy by B. J. Palmer, 1959 (Foreword)

Your speaker has a deeply embedded hope that what he is about to reveal will be clearly understood, accepted, and applied so that mankind will grasp the fullest significance of his relationships WITHIN himself.

What we shall explain WILL, in years to come, be accepted in toto as a working and workable plan. WE will not live to see that day, but our prophecy is that it WILL COME to pass; perhaps not possessed by OUR people, but by the great mass who will then know what WE NOW vividly and graphically foretell.

Our disclosures are what man seeks today in his closer communion in his companionship with his Creator for the betterment of all mankind, that he may take his place in the GREAT scheme of things which his Designer so masterfully and skillfully intended him to be and do.

In this busy age, in the days of so-called physical scientific research, it is surprising to find man restless, unsatisfied. Against all these confusing unsettled ups and downs, ins and outs, he seeks a harbor – some mental port to anchor himself which he can rely on a consistent and persistent understanding which will stay put. When he fails to find what he seeks, his mind refuses the challenge of change.

Who and what am I? Why am I here? Where do I fit into the great scheme of things? Who and what is the authority? There is an answer. It is the great majestic order of the universe and its obedience to unchanging law; the certainty and regularity of seasons; the march of the sun, moon, and stars; the regular coming of night and day, sun and darkness; between the balance of man's consumption of oxygen and its production of plant life; regularity of winter, spring, fall, and summer; the cry of a newborn child with its ever demonstration of abstract functional life.

This timeless, changeless order is an assurance of unchallenged authority; a sign of safe anchorage for the unsettled and undecided mind of man.

Increase in man's knowledge does not mean the discovery of new things, but only his insight into his understanding of himself and his ability to use that which already is, always has been – like the growth of a child from infant to adult man, who digs deeper discovering worlds within man, new to him but old in time. When these are realized man can and will face uncertainty, secure in knowledge, at peace within himself, because he will be at peace with the Almighty law of the Universal as well as the Unital law within each created unit.

B.J. with son Dave 1926

Book One: B.J. Palmer's Early Prophetic Period
Volumes 22-29; (1949-1953)

Starting with volume 22, The Bigness of the Fellow Within (1949), Palmer begins to discuss theology and enlightenment in detail. He relates this to the ancient principles of awakening and spirituality that he claims, for the first time, have now become practical because of the science of chiropractic.

Was there a source to this outpouring of writings, consisting of six texts, the smallest of which was about seven hundred pages? Perhaps it was due to the passing of his wife Mabel in 1948, or that his million dollar research clinic was in its ending days, perhaps it was his health at around age 70. Maybe he finally had some time after a career in politics and radio, and business, and the building of a new profession to reflect not only on his philosophy and art and science but his three trips around the world and his journeys to every sacred and holy place on planet earth. Or maybe he just awoke "as few men have before" and from his new level of consciousness, reflected on the ways in which others could also become enlightened to the spiritual insights that he was now able to embody. All that we have are his writings and his legacy. We do know that he wanted humanity to treasure these words even more than anything he had done.

B.J. and D.D. 1903

6

Part ~ 1: The Innate Transformation

Part one will look at the transformation of the educated mind being sublimated to the inner workings of the innate. This is a profound spiritual transformation that many would liken to a stage of enlightenment. There are two levels to this awakening according to B.J. The first is when the educated mind begins to acknowledge the profound and awesome nature of the innate intelligence within. This is marked by a turning away from an "outside in" approach to caring for the ills of the body and opening to a more "inside out" approach. I also consider this the Zen Koan of chiropractic, when the educated mind is asked to contemplate the shear wonder of the innate within.

The second aspect to the awakening, and this is more of the focus of this section, is when the educated mind humbles itself. The conscious thinking awareness stops trying to control and becomes more allowing of innate's processes. This is when the intelligence in and behind all things; is allowed to shine through and is sought for council and listened to for wisdom.

Later, I will explore this innate transformation in respect to genius, enlightenment, and B.J.'s inner transformation whereby he began to call himself "We" to represent the innate and the educated speaking as one. For part one, I will focus on the writings that direct the student to contact their innate, as well as the writings that discuss the importance of "finding oneself," and finally a section on B.J. discussing his early awakening, and how he "found himself." This awakening was different than his later enlightenment; here is when he begins the process of listening to innate as his guide through life.

B.J. 1910

7

Chapter 1

On Contacting Innate

One of the most interesting aspects of B.J.'s spiritual writings has to do with contacting Innate. To B.J. Innate was more than just the organizing intelligence in the body. It was also the inner striving towards order, which was inherent within the Intelligence that pervades the cosmos. It was God's voice, which was transmitted through Innate then to the conscious thinking brain, which could only be heard when the individual was receptive and ready.

His logic goes like this, if the intelligence of the universe could keep the planets in orbit and organize the intricacies of the living cell, it would stand to reason that it was also guiding the subtleties of intuition and instinct. The great problem, and this will be discussed in future chapters, was that man's educated brain got in the way and did not allow him to listen to this inner wisdom. This, B.J. will conclude was probably due to the vertebral subluxation, the distorted positioning of a vertebra which interfered with the free flow of mental impulse from the brain above to the body below and from God above to man below.

The first part of this chapter will deal with quotations that discuss the phenomenon of contacting Innate, or Innate contacting the educated thinking brain rather. The second part will show some of B.J.'s instructions on how to allow for this to happen.

v. 28 1952 Answers (pp. 67)

CAN YOU DO THIS?
Greatest service we can render mankind, and more particularly people of our profession, is to arouse within yourself a realization of greater Innate within each of you, that Innate may come forth from dark recesses of your understanding of yourself and into and become guiding light of YOUR life. Once YOU grasp this, received, you will pass this on to all you contact. If you do this, your and our life will have been enriched knowing the human race has been bettered for our having lived.

v. 22 1949 The Bigness of the Fellow Within (pp. 55)

How do you get into communion with your Innate? How do you get in tune with your Infinite? How does Educated contact Innate? You don't! *Innate communicates with you and when Innate is in contact you are in tune with the infinite. You* don't seek Innate. You don't go out on a hunting expedition, asking Innate to come to you. Innate *will seek you* when convinced you are ready to receive and will then come unsolicited.

As well ask: How can educated man contact God, get in communion with God, get in tune with the Infinite? How can man, the inferior, contact God, the superior; the servant, the master; the incompetent, the competent? It doesn't work that way. God contacts man, communicates with man, gets in tune with man. Man, however, religiously reverses the order. *He* talks to God; *he* thanks God; *he* suggests to God; *he* tells God what to do; *he* asks God for favors: *he* prays to God.

Education, so far as health problems and religious theories are concerned, works from outside in; from below upward. *Universal intelligence and Innate intelligence work from above downward, within outward....*

v. 28 1952 Answers (pp. 406)

Man Does not Contact God. God Contacts Man.
Man Does not Contact Innate.
Innate Contacts Man.
God Contacts Innate, Innate Contacts Educated.
All that Is Good, Worth While, Permanent, Comes from Above Down; Inside Out.
That Is THE Law.
Religions Reverse the Law.

.

v. 28 1952 Answers (pp. 67-68)

Often, education wants to know HOW to struggle or fight to attain "inspirations" from Innate. The *more* education struggles and fights to localize Innate to come thru, LESS he gets from Innate.

Many who read and study our writings re Innate frequently ask; "HOW can WE contact Innate? HOW can WE get in tune with innate? HOW can WE reach Innate?" This is equivalent to asking, "HOW can WE contact God; HOW can WE get in tune with God; HOW can WE reach God?" Let us reword those questions and perhaps that will help. "How can EDUCATION contact Innate or God; HOW can EDUCATION get in tune with Innate or God; HOW can EDUCATION reach Innate or God?" Answer is: EDUCATIONALLY, YOU CAN'T.

The above quotations are from 1949-1952; the quotations below are from 1955-1961. There is a marked difference in these two periods. The first is a discussion about contacting Innate. The second is filled with injunctions and instructions on how to do it. Some of these include Yoga, keeping a pen and pad by the bedside, meditation, sitting in nature, as well as cultivating an atmosphere of receptivity. B.J. who was now past 75 years of age was finally ready to share more with his readers about his awakening process. Originally, I was going to include these two periods of his writing in two separate volumes. I felt that this topical approach was more interesting. I hope you agree.

---

v. 37 1961 The Glory of Going On (pp. 71-72)

Let us make one point VERY clear, because the question is so often asked: "What CAN I DO to contact Innate ?" YOU can no more "contact Innate" than you can contact God with your babel of voices in pleas or prayers. If YOU are willing and receptive, and this factor IS PROVEN TO INNATE, INNATE WILL CONTACT YOU, if, as, and when Innate is ready. YOU cannot force an issue. It must come freely, willingly, and without pressure.

There will be those who will think I (the educated person) have turned mystic, whatever that is. There is nothing supernatural about this process of letting Innate contact YOU, except that it is quite unusual for Innate to contact Education. It is rare, therefore a much misunderstood process.

There is nothing "mystical" about Innate being in close and constant contact with tissue cell functions. Why, then, should it be considered "mystical" when Innate contacts educated brain delivering Innate thots TO educated brain, any more than it might be considered "mystical" when Innate contacts liver and produces bile, or contacts heart and pumps blood to and sucks it back from the body? One difference is that WE can't stop material functions in matter, but we do refuse to accept immaterial functions OF THOT as they come from Innate brain to educated brain.

The "secret" of this kid's success was that he had the courage to be himself, dared to constantly listen to Innate by preference, and act upon its flashes. He reached this conclusion at 18, and has been so directed ever since. The transitions from kid, to young man, to man, and now in the ripe age of maturity; and the more this man egotistically sublimated himself to the greater Innate, the more humble he became. He realized HIS education was like one drop of water to an Innate ocean. What he egoistically THOT he knew was like one grain of sand to the sea-shore. Innate proved there was a great unexplored world within him which needed understanding.

v. 38 1961 The Great Divide (pp. 67)

You cannot contact Innate, asleep or awake.
Innate CAN AND DOES contact EVERY tissue cell of your body, from birth to death, every second of time, even if function is normal or abnormal, in corresponding degrees depending upon interferences. The greater above always is more or less in contact with the lesser below. That is why, factually, in our humble opinion, all religions are NOT realistic. They try to EDUCATIONALLY reverse natural and normal law, from ABOVE-DOWN, INSIDE-OUT, either in *their* relations TO the Universe or the unit. They endeavor to present their convictions from OUTSIDE-IN, BELOW-UPWARDS.

v. 33 1955 Fame and Fortune (pp.115-116)

Long ago we learned that WHEN Innate thot-flashes came, they MUST BE accepted for full face value and acted upon AT ONCE, regardless whether we educationally thot they were right or wrong, good or bad, would or would not work. To do this was to humble education but we looked up to Innate and heeded its counsel.

WHEN do thot-flashes come from Innate to education? Anytime, day or night, when Innate knows conditions are JUST right. When and what ARE these "conditions"? They almost always come when education is least active, most absent, on a vacation. Many people find comfort and surcease in prayer in the quietness and solitude of a church where and when they think they are holding communion between themselves and their God, when in reality they are contacting more closely themselves to their own inner Innate selves. Possibly one is in the woods just sittin'; or he may be sittin' on the back porch looking at the river, smoking a good cigar; or he may be out fishin' where all is quiet and serene and all the hustling bustling city is miles away and is shut off from other cares and worries which jam clear thinking; or he might be playing golf miles from all disturbing influences but where he is surrounded with peace; or he might be asleep when education is totally absent and Innate can wake him to plant an "inspiration" as they are sometimes called.

Often we think of the yogis or mahatmas of India who sit for hours THINKING NOTHING, to receive SOMETHING WORTH WHILE. We have known propounders of world-wide movements to go off "into the silence" to meditate. It is when education IS MOST NON-COMMITTAL that Innate IS MOST COMMITTAL. When educated mind is quiescent, Innate sneaks in and plants thots worth while of vast human values. "Wasted time" doin' nothin', is oftentimes the most valuable time we spend.

Want to Let Innate Contact You?

It is when education is more nearly or totally blanked out that Innate gets in "thot flashes," because education is less liable to argue, debate, or deny them. (That's why WE have pad and pencil by our bedside.) The yogis of India have the RIGHT principle, mentally.

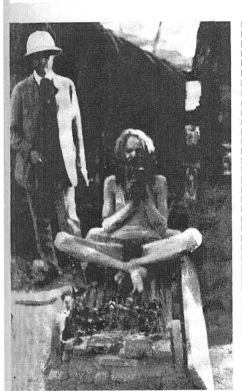

B.J. with Yogi on bed of nails in India 1925.

The sincere yogi would make an excellent Chiropractor for getting sick well IF he had knowledge and ability to correct the intermediary adjustment to restore power of internal Innate, to perfect greater understandings. Yogis assume what is, to each, the most RELAXED posture, which they assume for hours or days.

13

In this way, THEY attain the peace and poise of plenty, and become "In Tune With the Infinite."

B.J. with three holy men in India 1925.

The yogi endeavors to induce a semi sleep, by prolonged relaxation posture. Mahatma (teacher) Ghandi used this principle when he taught his people how to overcome their errors in breaking down 8,000 inconsistent castes including "untouchables." He was a simple man, with simple ways, thereby developing a great evolution.

(We are not advocating that chiropractors become yogis, altho there IS a certain group in our ranks who need yogiism to overcome ITS educated conflicts. We fear, however, they might even prostitute the purity of yoga. There are honest as well as dishonest yogis who peddle false philosophies, the same as some of our people peddle dangerous techniques, to grab dollars.)

And so we see, that this ability of B.J.'s to draw from the internal wisdom, was one of his very secrets to success. He learned to cultivate an inner guidance that was at once profound and certainly not ordinary. He will discuss for us in future chapters how this ability was used not only to grow his life of fame and fortune, but also to develop the art and philosophy of chiropractic and to deepen his own spirituality.

14

Chapter 2

On Finding Yourself

Finding yourself was one of B.J.'s great themes in his later years. He firmly believed that only the chiropractor that "found himself" could truly deliver the great service that is chiropractic. This inner knowing of finding oneself is directly related to the previous chapter, contacting innate. To B.J., these two were akin.

In these writings, it is obvious that B.J. clearly thought of Innate as at once the Soul and the sub-conscious all combined as one. He considered the great men of history; his one example here is Jesus, to have found themselves. In a later chapter on genius, we will see that he also relates this to Buddha, Mohammed, and other "great men." In these writings, B.J. considered Innate to be God within man. This will also be expanded on in several other chapters.

v. 22 1949 The Bigness of the Fellow Within (pp. 55)

WHAT IS "FINDING YOURSELF"?
To REALIZE THAT YOU and your education are very small things
—that your Innate within you is the all-important
—that to rely upon Innate doing through you is the *great* factor worth understanding.
You'll never find yourself by losing yourself.
You'll never find Innate within yourself by playing down Innate and playing up your education.
Every student in this or any other school has the *same* Innate potential that every other great person of history has had.
He can accomplish anything he wants to if he wants to long enough and strong enough.
But he will accomplish *nothing* until he *finds himself* with his Innate.
When he has, his great objective of life will be an open book before him
—nothing can hold him back
—he will take his place amongst the masters of men.
The teachings of Christ, regardless, were typical of a Man who *found himself.*   .

He went on the highways and by-ways, taking this gospel of helping men *find themselves,* as *He* found Himself.

Go ye and do likewise.

Go ye and *find yourself* and help the helpless multitudes find within themselves that great balm that, which it alone, gets them well.

---

v. 28 1952 Answers (pp. 76-77)

(Discussing the theme (with friends) of WHY some of our people succeed and *why* others fail, he raised this question: "Do you know OF ONE chiropractor who has adopted and adapted our Chiropractic philosophy, who FOUND HIMSELF in relation to his Innate, that ever repudiated that fundamental, or was a failure from any angle?" We named many—we couldn't mention ONE who lost face with himself, us or our profession.)

(It is plain what we mean by a "chiropractor" who LOST HIMSELF. He gropes, wanders, lost in the woods, has no mental compass, no rudder to steer his years. He thinks like a mental drunk. He is never anchored, he is flighty. He has eyes but cannot see; he has ears but cannot hear; he has feet but they run around in small and large circles. He is a round-around sucker for every gadget and treatment device. Each *is* what he *thinks* he needs. Each, given time, is another puzzle and mystery that solves nothing when applied. He has no powers of discernment or discrimination whether any, many or none are right or wrong. He seeks but never finds.

(He gropes, hunting for something, he knows not what. He suffers with inferiority complexes, thinking he knows what he knows when he knows he does not know. He refuses to admit limitations. Some day HE MAY find himself. When he does he IS a different man. He will then BE a success. When he FINDS HIMSELF he will know WHAT he knows and all heaven and hell cannot reverse his convictions. NOW HE KNOWS WHAT HE KNOWS…)

Absorb and blend Innate into education and you have found God. Many go to church Sunday, profess God; go home, deny and ignore Innate within, other 6 days. Preachers talk about a Super-

God which is outside, above and distant; and, scientists, psychiatrists and physicians discuss a "SUB-conscious" inside and within man.

Preachers should talk more about finding Innate, automatically making possible God contacting man. If preachers knew more Innate, they would know more about our "Soul." As well praise sun, denying moon, or vice-versa; or, immortalize day by ignoring night, or vice-versa—both are vitally necessary.

v. 22 1949 The Bigness of the Fellow Within (pp. 53-54)

Lying, usually buried, in us is an Innate Intelligence.
If we could open those flood gates and let Innate flow, we would be as good and as great as it, itself.
Lying in *all* of us is our Innate selves.
Innate *is* God in human beings *is* good in human beings *is* life in human beings *is* health in human beings *is* sane in human beings.
Let Innate flow in and through us and we can accomplish the great wonders.

All of us want to be big; do big things; make the world better because of our having lived in it.
The vast majority want to be big by *thinking they are big,* by theorizing about big things, thinking external education alone is sufficient and is all important.

Until he has *found himself,* nothing happens.
When man has *found himself,* he steps out of the mass, gets into the class, and then begins to climb the ladder of accomplishment.
All men and women who have left their imprint on the years of time, to the benefit of the world, were ones who *had* found themselves.

No matter how many years we exist by cluttering up this earth on which we move and have our being, we will never reach maturity until such time as the educated fellow on the outside is as big and as great as the Innate inside.

17

"Suffer little children to come unto me, for such is the Kingdom of Heaven" was but another way of saying that we *are* educationally "little children" and we should go to Innate within "for of such *is* the Kingdom of Heaven."

---

v. 23 1950 Up From Below the Bottom (pp. 395)

EVERY MAN AND WOMAN has vision.
Every man and woman also has illusions.
Betwixt and between are one or more "blind sides."
Rare is the balanced individual.
Our vision is YOUR illusion.
Your ILLUSION is OUR vision.
We will hunt YOUR vision. Will YOU hunt for OURS?
Thus, both submerge our illusions.
That man has LOST HIMSELF who buries himself in his illusions and refuses to dig out.
That man FOUND HIMSELF who climbs up on his vision, and helps lift others to become masters of men.
Where are YOU in this great equation?

Let not your language speak, for it is often used to conceal thot.
Let not your education speak, for it is too frequently used to evade truth.
Let not that varnish veneered self answer, for it is too often used to camouflage the real fellow.
Put all your mind thru the acid test.
Go back to that bottom of your heart of hearts.
Scratch every hidden crevice of your soul.
Let your conscience, with which you expect to face your God, test you all ways, always.
Listen to that wee sma' voice that talks to you at 3:00 a.m.

The Same, No Difference

When any person has "found himself" in relation to himself, it remains the same—call it by what name you please.
Knowing yourself is when you understand and know the Innate within.

It is becoming more and more evident as the writings make plain, that B.J.'s message was very spiritual. It was about connecting to your deepest inner self. He even went so far as to say that contacting God in church was more likely contacting your inner self. That innate is just an aspect of God, was his main point.

That wee sma' voice, is, to B.J., the sage of the ages. It is the source of all genius, wisdom, and inspiration. Since all human's have an innate intelligence which organizes and keeps their body's healthy as possible, then so too, could each individual contact the innate within for inner guidance and wisdom. It is there that one can truly "find oneself."

B.J. 1900

Chapter 3
BJ on Finding Himself

These writings on contacting innate and finding oneself are not just theoretical, B.J. is writing from direct experience. This chapter examines his own autobiographical writings about how he found himself.

B.J. was 14 years old in 1895, when his father, D.D. Palmer, the magnetic healer of eight years discovered chiropractic. The quest for an answer to the question as to the role of innate intelligence in the body and in the cosmos at large became B.J.'s life's mission. The Chiropractic Zcn-Koan of innate intelligence was asked for the first time, and B.J. spent the next sixty years searching for an answer.

In this chapter, B.J. writes about his early experiences of "finding himself" at ages 17, 18, and 19. Which age it was does not really matter. The fact of the matter is that something significant happened that allowed him to trust his inner wisdom more and more. He may not have yet realized the scope of this realization, but in these later years he reflects on the experience, and makes it plain that he was changed forever.

Palmer's early influences were his father and a mesmerist or hypnotist that B.J. traveled with for some time. The combination of his father's influence which was significant and professor Flint's ability to induce in the young B.J. profound hypnotic states, allowed him to access an inner depth that is rare. Also, B.J. was privy to his father's discussions and notes. D.D. Palmer was well read in medical texts as well as spiritualism, mesmerism, transcendentalism and Confucianism. All of these sparks combined launched B.J. on a lifelong inner quest. It was this ability to access the innate wisdom that he sought to pass on.

---

v. 22 1949 The Bigness of the Fellow Within (pp. xix-xx)

At seventeen, he "found himself."
This boy had no education.
Educationally, as the world understands it, he was far short.
Innately, he had the wisdom of the ages working for him, with him.

Day after day, week after week, month after month, we listened to D. D. propound ideas. We drank them in, hungrily. In time, they percolated and we became saturated with their value. In time, we "found ourself", all of which has been written in various of our publications.

1906

In 1902, D. D. Palmer issued us a diploma signed by himself, his wife, and ourself. We practiced Chiropractic since we were seventeen, calling ourself "Doctor." That was the why and wherefore of mustache and beard—to appear older than our years. We thot we could disguise youth because sick people did not want to go to a boy with a new idea they knew nothing about. We practiced in those early years in Lake City, Iowa; Traverse City and Manistique, Michigan; Elkins, Belington, and Kernes, West Virginia, etc. We mention this here because it has a direct bearing on the character and life of D. D. Palmer, later.

21

v. 22 1949 The Bigness of the Fellow Within (pp. xix-xx)

At seventeen, he "found himself."

This boy had no education.

Educationally, as the world understands it, he was far short.

Innately, he had the wisdom of the ages working for him, with him.

This boy was not educated as that term is commonly understood and believed necessary.

He claims to have a bit of knowledge and wisdom about the natural ways of life and living.

He had little schooling out of books, semesters, diplomas, etc.

He has had a tremendous opportunity to work with Innate in giving others a natural and normal understanding of life and health.

People who have sat at the feet of this boy, and now man, who have drunk at his fountain, and who accept his teachings, go away from here with something more than a formal education, more than a means of punching backbones, more than a means of making a living, more than amassing a fortune.

They have learned a better way to live with themselves and with others, a means and method of intercommunicating within themselves, to draw out from within the greater self that usually lies buried, thus developing a greater person with which to live throughout their more than normal span.

v. 28 1952 "Answers" (pp. 79)

If it were a method of transplanting or pilastered education like so much veneer, WHERE WOULD ANY CHIROPRACTOR BE TODAY? There wouldn't be ONE if it hadn't been for the ONE MAN who was expelled from high school in first half of first year. All have directly or indirectly sat at his feet, learned what he thot and taught, have what they have because of so-called ignorance of this self-made man who inherently inherited a lost cause from his father. This man dedicated and consecrated his life to the development of self-drawing out the unlimited Innate resources within himself, to carry on this great work. That HE has succeeded is self-evident. Fortunately, at age eighteen he FOUND HIMSELF.

Because of HIS having lived, millions of years have been added to millions of lives. Because of HIS teachings, he has brot millions of dollars into pockets of thousands of Chiropractors. Grateful? Many are! Many are not! Many nurse petty grudges because of actions necessary to be done as they obstructed his path of duty. Many others nursed mental bruises as he was compelled to brush aside obstacles. Common sense has taught many others such aggressive actions were inevitable, at those times, in those manners. None of these viewpoints have ever deterred this man from pursuing his relentless course.

v. 37 1961 The Glory of Going On (pp. 56)

HOW did all of this come about? Was it accident, happen-stance, good luck; or was it based on sound rational methods of approach and deliveries? At the age of 18 (when this author FOUND HIMSELF) he observed that an Innate INTERNAL to LIVING man contacted EVERY tissue cell, EVERY second, with EVERY organ in the living human body, from ABOVE-DOWN, INSIDE OUT...

B.J. in Wat Chang, Bangkok

23

v. 37 1961 The Glory of Going On (pp. 59)

It was when he FOUND HIMSELF in his relations with his INNER SUPER-SELF, he decided to LISTEN TO INNATE MORE, and give LESS attention to education, especially in gaining a knowledge of self, **within** himself, thereby gaining a greater knowledge of **what** made man tick in relation to his studies of life, health, sickness, and act upon ITS advices when thot-flashes came thru in a split second.

This young man found there existed a world-wide breach between Innate people AND educated people. The small group were non-conformists. The large group were conformists. When Innate's thot-flashes came thru to smaller group, from ABOVE-DOWN INSIDE-OUT, larger group of educated people developed OUTSIDE-IN BELOW-UP innumerable complex arguments, de-bates, compromises, endeavoring to prove smaller group were wrong, and there WAS NO SUCH THING. The larger group worried, stewed, fretted-days, weeks, months, and years—to prove smaller group were wrong.

v. 37 1961 The Glory of Going On (p. 71)

That, plus the development this boy-man made in Innate's natural and normal CHIROPRACTIC, under the guidance of Innate thot-flashes, made HIM realize HE must dedicate and consecrate HIS life to teaching the Chiropractic profession to succeed in like manner, by explaining as best he could that WHAT had occurred in him could occur in others, because they contained same Innate as he, and they could also climb out of mediocrity same as he had.

Then that state of his understanding had been reached and he had FOUND HIMSELF, he began to teach others how they, too, COULD find themselves. Until he passed on to others this transition beyond himself, and they caught his understanding of the process, life became a boundless field of human service. He was as one inspired, as tho he had discovered a wonderful exhaustless fount of wisdom which anybody else could tap as he tapped it.

v. 37 1961 The Glory of Going On (pp. 247)

His successor who, by right of inheritancy, formulated THIS LAW OF LIFE into consciousness in the minds of man, presented its postulates, methods of sources and expressions. He presented in millions of sick tangible proof of the correctness of those deductions. This man dared to be a NONconformist; a firm adherent who took his father's PRINCIPLE and, developed it into a sound philosophy, practice of science and art, which worked when worked with sincerity when properly applied. This man, at the age of eighteen, "found himself" in relation to this fundamental principle.

v. 39 1961 Our Masterpiece (pp. 116-117)

At the age of 19 (when this author FOUND HIMSELF) he observed that an Innate Intelligence INTERNAL to LIVING man contacted EVERY tissue cell, EVERY second, with EVERY organ in the *living* human body, from ABOVE DOWN, INSIDE OUT. This Innate sent messages, via nerves, from brain to body; told each cell WHAT to do, and received reply messages in return, whether it was or was not done, all the time from birth to death.

Any *internal* intellectuality great enough to build what is estimated to be 400 trillion human tissue cells, formulate specific organs to do specific duties, locate them in respective groups, correlate these systems into specific over-all duties, start ALL working TOGETHER harmoniously, is great enough for our comparatively insignificant education to listen to, IF WE COULD GET IT to tell US what WE should and should not know; how, when, where to do its bidding. It has succeeded in doing right things, right ways, for millions of people, for aeons of time; therefore, should be good enough guide, informant, and teacher for us. It would be wisdom on OUR part TO LISTEN, heed, take advice and suggestions FROM Innate TO education.

If Innate was immaculate enough to conceive, build, direct, control, regulate, and repair the building of a new complete unit of a child in utero 280 days, surely it was immaculate enough to tell the pretty education of a few short years what to do, where, when, and why.

---

v. 39 1961 Our Masterpiece (pp. 135)

Many times, some of our educated people in our Palmer Enterprises tell US not to do this this way, but do it that way, meaning of course WE should follow THEIR educated methods of presentation. At such times, we must decide whether to follow suggestions offered by our Innate by preference, rejecting THEIR educated presentations. When they remain with us long enough, they will learn the LAW OF INNATE'S PRESENTATIONS. When they DO, they will understand why we feel it necessary to reject their educated opinions.

This ends the section on the Innate Transformation. Here we found the inner circumstances that led to B.J.'s success and mostly we are shown the zeal and style with which he communicated to his followers, colleagues, and students. There is something unique that B.J. passed down to his followers, not generally found in a health profession. This was the awesome and incredible majesty of the innate intelligence. Too often, that is his only legacy half-remembered by the profession philosophically or spiritually. Here we see, that B.J. taught with greater depth than previously realized by many. His message was one of awakening.

In the next sections, we will see how B.J. extended his spiritual insights into the realm of religion. Mostly we will find his conviction that this inner voice was access to the great intelligence that pervades all of the cosmos. Here he will critique science, medicine, and religion as being stuck in narrow perspectives that are mostly dictated by their conscious minds, their "educated intelligences," not by their inner knowing, by the soul within.

Part II
Prayer and God

This section examines two pieces of B.J.'s writings on spirituality. It shows a discussion of the futility of prayer, as a means to control the intelligence of creation. He then attempts to prove a God that is at once transcendent and immanent by arguing the shear magnificence and wonder and intelligence of creation.

1931

1956

27

Chapter 4
On Prayer

To B.J., prayer was too often wasted. This attitude was based on several of his insights. The first was that it was useless for the inferior creation to ask the superior creator to change anything. After all, was not the creator all wise? How could it make mistakes? Especially since all health in the body was already bestowed upon the living form if only the obstruction to this flow of infinite health and wisdom was removed. If that obstruction, namely, the vertebral subluxation was not removed, then God could not even get through to heal the body thus prayed for. And prayer was most likely unnecessary if the adjustment was performed. This is all because the health and communication that flows from above down and within out, is a basic law of nature like gravity.

Secondly, asking for forgiveness was a waste of time to a creator that already knew all details of the sin per se. Thirdly, how could people have the audacity to pray on Sunday, and not acknowledge the great majesty of the innate within on the other six days of the week (especially if they are using medicines and thus denying innate's healing powers)? To B.J. medicine and prayer often fell into the same category.

Lastly, and this is rarely mentioned, but important to note in the historical context, to B.J. every thought or thot, was a prayer, and had the power of action. And one action that was a pure expression of prayer was the chiropractic adjustment.

Also in this chapter, Palmer's unique writing style becomes apparent. Some of these passages are difficult to read. This is not due to the lack of context of the larger passage. It is due to his difficult style.

---

v. 22 1949 The Bigness of the Fellow Within (pp. 64)

Here is a situation apropos. People involved are two: a minister and a physic-ian.

The educated minister was educated in an educated college to study the soul, how to pray to and for its salvation, etc.

The educated physician was educated in an educated medical college to study the material body, how to apply materia medica, etc.

The minister becomes sick. Does he take the sick *body* to another minister of the soul?

He goes to a physician who diagnoses his condition as "liver complaint." The liver is matter.

The physic-ian prescribes some other kind of matter for his material liver, hoping to so change the material liver as to get it back to its normal mate-rialistic liver condition.

The physic-ian commits some sort of what he calls a "sin." It worries his "conscience."

Does he take his erring conscience, his sin, to another physic-ian like himself?

He takes his soul to a minister of souls, who can help him eradicate the evils of sin.

Simple as the divisions are, they each contain elements which deny themselves.

The minister eats, digests, and otherwise moves about daily in a material body.

The physic-ian thinks, senses, interprets, and otherwise uses his mind to exist with.

So, each admits the necessity of both *being together,* yet each denies they *are* together when anything goes hay-wire with either. The Chiropractor does not tell the educated minister or physic-ian to have faith, or pray to anything for anything, to get well.

Neither does he tell the educated mind of either what to eat, what to take, or how to take it.

The Chiropractor does not add or subtract anything to or from the educated mind or its body.

---

v. 23 1950 Up From Below The Bottom (pp. 22)

Remember the weekday, to keep it holy.

Why pray cream on Sunday and live skimmed milk the rest of the week?

29

v. 23 1950 Up From Below The Bottom (pp. 2)

Religions recognize "God" Sunday in churches and in mouthings in prayer. In theory, they condescend to concede such other six days of the week. We also know these people go to medical men week days, who deny Innate Intelligence in man. Medical men pray to God on Sunday and say "nature cures" other six days of the week, and then deny there is a "nature" WITHIN man when they rip out "unnecessary organs;" they look for causes and cures in pills, powders, and potions OUTSIDE human body; and laugh and hurl sarcasm at Chiropractor who recognizes Innate Intelligence WITHIN man as the all-wise, omnipotent, omniscient, omnipresent Director-General who asserts that THE ONLY possible cause and cure are WITHIN man.

Why this inconsistent variable of "believing" one thing one day and denying same thing other six? Answer is simple: lack of KNOWLEDGE of constancy of Innate constant such as Chiropractic preaches AND practices, as well as medical inability TO PROVE such exists as Chiropractor proves every day, on every case he adjusts. Many so-called Chiropractors PREACH Innate constant and PRACTICE medical variables. Many other so-called Chiropractors PREACH medical variables and PRACTICE Chiropractic constant. A few Chiropractors preach AND practice Innate constant.

---

v. 28 1952 "Answers" (pp. 308 & 408)

Why pray cream on Sunday and live skimmed milk the rest of the week?

Sick People Pray for Power when thru Us Would Flow a Universal Power if We Would Permit It.

---

v. 24 1950 Fight To Climb (pp. 520-21)

Trend of this story bears largely on religion, which is also a problem. We are surrounded by people who BELIEVE in efficacy of prayer; that they can and do talk to God, God listens to them and answers their prayers—sometimes. If they are sick, they can pray to God and God will make them whole. They do not reason that, so long as God cannot get thru an obstruction, God cannot heal. Neither do they use logic that God is superior and their education that prays is inferior, and inferior cannot talk to superior.

Does Chiropractor resist possible invasion of demands upon God by prayer as against Chiropractic adjustment, restoring natural internal potentials that are there IF they can act? Or, does he take hardest path and explain how law works, under what conditions it works, under what conditions it cannot work, and how sick people do get well—prayer or not, to contrary? Verily, to live WITH CHIROPRACTIC is a question of resistance and/or invasion as to which does which to which.

B.J., Mabel, Dave, & guides, Gizah/Sphinx, 1925

v. 24 1950 Fight To Climb (pp. 537-8)

Recently, many nations have been at war. Each prayed ITS way to SAME God, each asking, and saying that God is on HIS side. The UI pursues its constructive purpose, regardless.

Any thot, idea, request, appreciation, implied or expressed, is a prayer. To concentrate upon ANY subject, to logically sustain or prove untrue reality of subject thot upon, whether religious or otherwise, is a prayer. Thinking puts thot into action, thus making theory into stronger action, whether called a prayer or not, whether within an edifice or out in the great wide open spaces.

We have listened to preachers' sermons. They appear to get a "kick" out of thinking they ARE PREACHING a line of reasoning. Which THEY HOPE is helping mankind. All they say goes out of THEIR mind INTO mind of listener—and there it stops for want of a practical way to put preachment into practical use. Chiropractor DOES NOT PREACH a sermon. He PRACTICES a reality, permitting that which IS PREACHED about to work its salvation internally without interference.

We have watched Chiropractors practicing a reality of a religion. They should get a "thrill" out of knowing they are PRACTICING a line of action which IN REALITY is helping mankind. All they can do is to make it possible to open channels for natural expression of law.

We find no fault with prayer. If patient gets satisfaction out of praying, we would raise no objection. Neither would we insist that he DO pray before he CAN get well. Prayer neither helps nor hurts, hurries nor hinders his recovery.

We do not oppose religion. We oppose churchianities built into it by preachers, which have all but destroyed religion.

We do not oppose Chiropractic. We oppose imponderable barnacles fastened on to it by "chiropractors", which tend to destroy Chiropractic.

32

We are for religion, unrestricted, same as we are for Chiropractic in natural and true state. We are for ships and precious cargoes they carry, but we are opposed to millions of barnacles which empirically attach themselves, which oppose their rapidly reaching their destination, wherever that is.

---

v. 24 1950 Fight To Climb (pp. 541)

To Know Is Knowledge
Analysts who give this subject study will think they see a conflict in philosophy, facts, and application. We have advocated futility of prayer, uselessness of asking for more of something from a higher source. We have said that vertebral subluxation prevents it getting to them WITHOUT prayer; that it is useless and unnecessary to ask for something which could and would flow naturally, normally, and fully, were it not because of this physical obstruction between brain and body, mind and function. If there is water in tank, if hose is attached to faucet, if faucet is open so water CAN flow, it is not necessary to pray for water.

---

v. 24 1950 Fight To Climb (pp. 692-93)

We have been a student of man all our life and may know every possible principle of life and death but that does not give us the inside track or make it possible to side-track errors committed; neither does God permit us to suggest or dictate to Thon what to do, when or how; we are still a servant same as sinner.

Suppose God were some high, big personage, running this world; he was a male being with anatomy like unto us except larger. Suppose we should ask for a special favor—to change equator to here in winter and in summer bring down North Pole—would He do it? Suppose we had an idea some person had been bad—functions went wrong—all his life—would our asking God forgive be a success? It seems unreasonable for a 1-year-old to demand of his 50-year-old father what to do—and more unreasonable for a 50-year-old critter to plead, beg, offer incense, holler his head off, lay himself prone with deliberation, stand up, sit down, a few times, look imploringly at a stick of wood, thinking that all such will have some effect in getting this almighty Great and Good God to change His opinion on some detail he thinks ought to be changed. Does ant ask chargings to suit its convenience?

Can it be that God made this world, manufactured everything that was, is or will be in it; regulates where we come from, where we go and what we do while here; that He can hold endless planets in space and then doesn't know enuf to put your misdeeds where they belong after you have committed them? Suppose you commit murder—don't Thon know it? Assuming he doesn't, you "take it to the Lord, thy God." You tell Him what you did, why you did it, and how, thinking He was asleep when you did it. After you explained all circumstances—which Thon already knew—you ask for forgiveness. If Thon thinks you deserve it, Thon will give it, otherwise not—and knowing all circumstances better than you such would be done whether or not you brot it to Thon.

What you need is some smooth, soft, sweet smelling salve to balm your educated reasoning. That's as far as your desires should demand—further than that is solely and entirely within province of God. Do you call it reformation because you change the way to get at same personage with same intent in view—for Thon to change to your pleasure? If that's religious reformation—then it's going on.

---

v. 28 1952 Answers (pp. 87)

MAN IS EGOTISTIC
Man, in egotistic and often ego maniac education, assumes to think he knows Universal Intelligence, all its attributes, and suggests and tries to direct and run it. His prayers for more power, his directions to the Universal Power, his thanks for what he has received, portray that. Man, also, in his egotistic education, assumes to think he knows the Innate Intelligence within…

v. 28 1952 Answers (pp. 417)

Prayer Is Affirmation to Education to Bolster Education's Theories of God.

---

v. 34 1957 Fame and Fortune (pp. 63)

Further conflict is religious concept that we can talk UP TO God, ask for and secure favors and things WE "educationally" WANT; and talk UP TO God and THANK HIM for favors WE think He grants in reply to our "educated" requests; and CHIROPRACTIC concept that ALL which is good, right, normal, flows from ABOVE DOWN, from WITHIN OUTWARD, and nothing WE "educationally" think we **artificially** ask for or receive **naturally** increases or decreases normality of that which we are ENTITLED to receive WITHOUT asking or thanking for. During two World Wars, both sides asked God for victory.

---

v. 34 1957 Evolution or Revolution? (pp. 70)

To ascribe to D. D. Palmer THE PRINCIPLE of interference with the normal quantity flow of transmission of an Innate mental impulse nerve force flow between brain and body is too narrow an interpretation of the NEW PRINCIPLE he announced. Like electricity, Innate Intelligence ALWAYS has existed, but never was acknowledged or admitted as a factor of life or health WITHIN man. Peculiarly, all religions admit existence of a Superior God—whatever each construes that to be. Christian Science acknowledges such is fundamental in health. In so doing, however, they approach this inherent all-powerful INNER power by EXTERNAL PRAYER FROM OUTSIDE of another person, therefore the SAME **OLD** PRINCIPLE STILL PREVAILS.

---

v. 39 1961 Our Masterpiece (pp. 133)

PALMER'S LAW OF LIFE PHILOSOPHY, as propounded and presented in our Vol. XXXVI, is not in any loose or strict sense of a term a religion, per se. There are those who have tried to interpret it as such. This philosophy acknowledges a Superior and Supreme Universal Intellectual Law which many call "God." Religions, including all, their beliefs, faiths, rituals and ceremonials, plead, beg, ask for, and utter prayers from OUTSIDE IN, BELOW UP, for same purpose and in same manner as does medicine. In this sense, "educated" religious devotees think they possess some in accessible rights and privileges, of "educationally" asking for, telling, or advising this "Supreme Being" HOW to instruct IT to regulate and govern all affairs of mere man on earth, or how to advise IT to govern all things celestial.

To B.J. prayer is often used by the conscious thinking mind to try and control rather then allowing the innate truth to come forth naturally. I wonder how he would respond to clinically controlled trials that show how prayer helps the recovery process after surgery? He would probably acknowledge that innates can speak with each other. To him, anything that is in accord with natural law is not a miracle, just normal.

Chapter 5
On God (writings from 1949-1952)

Palmer's discussion of God is central to his spirituality. His entire premise is based on it. He does prefer the term Universal Intelligence to God. One wonders how this might fit into the classic great chain of being, where intelligence is an outer aspect of God, beyond that, life and matter, within that, soul and pure spirit.

For the first time reader, it might be more enjoyable to study the shorter passages, thereby gaining a good understanding of B.J.'s insights. This will adequately prepare you for the coming chapters. For the more advanced student or second time reader, the longer passages are worth the time. I have placed them at the end of the chapter. Please keep in mind that all of these passages were selected from much longer discussions. Future chapters will examine the evolution of Palmer's conceptualization of God. This chapter is organized according to the green book's volume number.

---

v. 22 1949 The Bigness of the Fellow Within (pp. 22)

Within all natural animals, including man and woman, courses in active flow the wisdom of all time, the sage of the ages, call it what you may— Universal Intelligence, God, Jehovah, etc.

v. 22 1949 The Bigness of the Fellow Within (pp. 29)

They say the soul of man was made in the image and likeness of the Creator. Not GOD, but GODlike, in its attributes. The soul of man reflects the attributes of GOD as a mirror reflects sunlight. GOD is ever-present and His attributes are omniscience and omnipotence, and as man reflects these attributes he grows in the image and likeness of the Creator.

They say the five senses, by which the materialist proves his world, are shadow senses, ephemeral and mortal, and that the real world is the eternal world of spirit....

Man reflects these divine qualities as a mirror reflects the sunlight; but unlike the mirror, he grows in the image and likeness of the qualities he reflects. There is something in man that recognizes these eternal things, and that something is not his chemical elements, but his GODlike self.

I say, "My body, my mind, my soul, my coat, my shoes, my watch." I use the possessive case. Why?
Am I my body, my mind, and my soul?
Or are these instruments I use, as I use my coat, my shoes, and my watch?
What is this something within that wills to do a thing? *What* urges the body and mind forward?
What is it that has driven us upward, from the sea slime, to dominion over ourselves?

v. 22 1949 The Bigness of the Fellow Within (pp. 32)

Nor have we reasons for believing the limit of its evolution has been reached. Driven by an insatiable desire, urged by the realization that there are yet myriads of harmonies which are not registered by our present senses, this inward something will evolve new senses, until the human mind and soul reflect, with greater accuracy, the qualities of the all-knowing, ever-present, all-powerful principle we call God.

v. 22 1949 Bigness (pp. 36)

We *know* there *is* a Universal Intelligence—call it "God" if you wish. We *know* there *is* an Innate Intelligence in the unit—be it tree, bird, reptile, animal, or man. The evidence is everywhere surrounding us and in us. This evidence appeals to reason, logic, common sense, and facts. It is not necessary to "believe" or "have faith" in those facts.

v. 22 1949 Bigness (pp. 117)

GREAT IS THE SOURCE
GOD IS A NAME mankind ascribes to an intellectual law that creates, governs, runs all living things; has run the world for a long, long time. Has done a good job of it. Within the accomplished fact is a better judgment than man could substitute with all his

38

intelligence. "The Kingdom of God is within you"; the God of the Universe of which we are a part. Anything and everything the God of the Universe knows is potential knowledge within us.

God knows all, sees all, is all. Therefore, mankind represents that which knows all, sees all, is all. We are a manifestation of it, as it has worked through us.

---

v. 23 1950 Up From Below the Bottom (pp. 298)

You ask for proofs of unwritten law. Creator of man is NOT like man, because a powerless creature cannot create another being. The maker must possess attributes that make in beginning as well as now. We cannot make a God, yet reverse is true. Can creator be perfect and creation abnormal? Yes.

---

v. 24 1950 Fight to Climb (pp. 507)

Therefore, II becomes THE beginning of man's understanding of the man world with which he lives, and association of others like himself with whom he associates.

When man thinks of Source, where he came from, how he came, or where he goes upon death, he thinks in terms of The Great Spirit, Jehovah, or perhaps God. Thinking of "God" he has been taught to believe in a great heroic man, a He or Him *male* being with gigantic *human* possibilities. Man is prone to think of God in terms of himself, like himself, except only a greater self. Man tries to make God more man-like, when, in reverse, man should try to make man more God-like. We prefer thot of a Universal Law; therefore, being abstract without shape or form, the term UNIVERSAL INTELLIGENCE.

When man thinks of himself, and that within himself which makes him tick and run methodically and systematically, he calls it "nature," "instinct," or "subconscious mind," which is an evasion or refusal to acknowledge that within him is the same Law Source as is in the Universe—an Innate Unital Law; therefore, being abstract, term INNATE INTELLIGENCE.

v. 26 1952 Conflicts Clarify (pp. 125)

Even tho we study it from this standpoint, we must again refer back to THE essential which CAUSED this to take place—the one great, creative, infinite intelligence itself, known under various names. Theologist calls it God; you might call it the worldly conscious mind. There is more freedom in Universal Intelligence than our names give credit for.

v. 27 1952 History Repeats (pp. 46)

Man is peculiar—a combination of intelligences. In starting points we universally acknowledge a God, and beneath is an Innate Intelligence. We say "beneath" yet don't wish to imply that, altho as we view the world we are forced to admit there is one intelligence over all others. There is one Universal Intelligence so great in its common law that it can cause trees to grow in Mexico and Canada, Africa and Asia, and cause animals to expand in every country on the globe…

v. 28 1952 Answers (pp. 91)

IS IT "HE?"
This Universal Intelligence takes many attributes in the human educated mind. Usually, in our modern day, it is a He and a Him of tremendous size, equivalent to and something like ourselves. Others see it only in the abstract, without shape, form, or size. Whatever this IT has been or is, It has existed from the beginning of time. It has directed all worlds, all forms, all created things, including mankind.

v. 28 1952 Answers (pp. 299)

We are coming to think of God as dwelling in man, rather than as operating on man from without.

Below are the longer quotes. These are important to include because they lay out the discussion in greater detail and really give the flavor of B.J.'s unique style. Also, these quotes discuss the role of vertebral subluxation and begin to describe for us B.J.'s conception of natural law.

v. 23 1950 Up From Below the Bottom (pp. 331-2)

"What is the Lord's work?" What is meant by term "Lord?" Man is of two minds—Innate and Educated—both being parts of one whole. When asked who built your child, you answer "Nature," implying intelligence superb in scope and character. When pinioned, you admit that "only infinity could do the likes of that." As children are born everywhere, we concede a mind universal is doing that; hence "Nature" is a broad term used in trees, vegetables, animals, and man; therefore, term in its last analysis is God.

Innate Intelligence in man is a focalized God. God personifies in man, plants, and animals; hence we are products of the God mind behind us. Bible uses "Lord" and "God" as synonymous and makes no distinction. If God is a synonymous term and used in same sense, then we, as Chiropractors, use term Universal Intelligence as same as God. God is a name used to express this supreme intelligence.

Man considers this something which is much greater than Intelligence of man as a great BIG MAN. Therefore, God, in your mind, shapes himself into a man-shaped God that is everywhere present. Upon second thot, he would use "God" to express INTELLIGENCE, same as if you would ask us to shape Innate Intelligence. It is a condition without form. When bringing terms to LAST analysis you say, "God" is a name we use to attempt to personify Universal Intelligence.

When Chiropractor starts in his cycles with God, Universal Intelligence and Lord are synonymous terms and of the same fundamental thot.

"What is the mission of Universal Intelligence?"

"To build this world; to keep it builded; to rebuild it when it dies; to keep this world constantly shaping to highest idealized form. To make, create, or individualize itself into Innate Intelligences." Innate Intelligence is a sunbeam, a ray of light from sum total of lights or sum total of senses. It is not an individual portion, yet it is.

v. 24 1950 Fight To Climb (pp. 673-76)

GOD IS HEALTH—all life is given, all death is taken by thon. It is a condition man cannot abridge, repeat or duplicate, give or take, reduce or increase, in part or whole, in speck or cosmos. It has its own comings and goings. We can neither add it to a body nor take away.

Health is not in a pill or an operation. God does not wrap Himself within prescription papers, poisons; lock Himself in when the cork is plugged, or jump in when rips are made and prefer being sewed in after stitches are taken.

All health, law and morality we desire for ourselves, friends or enemies must come uninterrupted from a source unto all alike, upon which all do agree and in a way beyond all dispute or question—from subconscious, self-subliminal, self-mature, instinct, Vis Medicatrix Naturae, soul, spirit, or Innate Intelligence of Chiropractor. These terms have one and same meaning, they individualize the inner self— the God within man. Innate Intelligence is a Universal Intelligence and that is man-God.

When we want essence of law, truth or health, we go back to God. We agree upon that common viewpoint; and we want to, step by step, proceed from universally accepted opinions to those upon which we differ. At present, your minds are in a quandary—not that you DON'T agree, not that you QUESTION our statement, but because THE MANNER in which it is presented is different. Understand clearly, we have not denied God; on reverse, have proven it is the logical, consistent and reasonable beginning of our message.

You will concede if we could hypothesize a man who had no vertebral subluxations, his Innate Intelligence would be free to act in his body, as IT desired. If spirit be free to come and go at its own inclination, desire or will, its body would be materialistic counterpart of immaterial. Body would do what mind willed. If Innate Intelligence is Health and Innate flows freely to all parts of body, then body duplicates, in action, what Innate will in thot, WHICH WOULD BE HEALTH. Then man must be healthy.

Tank may be full of water, hose in proper conduction condition and connected, and all of flower bed with its bushes ready to receive; but so long as faucet is turned off—nothing doing. Turn on faucet, doing of which does not add or subtract to given quantity or quality of water—it gives the principle of gravitation, freedom to flow water from where stored to where needed. That is all you accomplish when adjusting a subluxation, is to give freedom to innate Intelligence, so INNATE may personify itself in organs of body.

You are trying to permit a re-establishment of a closer union between Innate Intelligence (immaterial) and stomach, liver, or spleen (materialities) for purpose of establishing equilibrium—HEALTH, all of which was in abundance at source and would be at terminal if it could get there. If you have not established this purpose in your Chiropractic mind, your adjustments are a cipher as regards your purpose of doing things.

Health part of message we teach, perhaps not quite as broadly as stated, but in sum and substance, you accept as purpose of Chiropractic—to make man healthy. To that extent you are taught; that part you grasp, accept, understand and practice. Should we step forth boldly and declare that adjustment of a vertebral subluxation was for ultimate purpose of permitting closer communion between God and man you would decry our premise, not because you could logically disprove or deny one iota, but because it was a new viewpoint you have never considered, therefore subject to hasty criticism.

Let us make our next premise. Imagine another individual, if you will, whom we hypothesize, who has no subluxations, whose Innate is free to act; THEN THAT MAN REPRESENTS PERSONIFIED LAW, and that man could not do wrong. God being law, God being in man, God being free to flow in man, man must be the action of thot. Thot could be no more or less than law itself. Man would be law as expressed. Law is proper thing to do under proper circumstances. It is individualistic, then communistic, then universal. All constant law is founded upon God, then from man to man, then to all men.

Value of statutes is defined as; "Those STATUTES are most valuable which express the common opinion of common people on a common subject"; but "Law is individualized expression of God thru a composite form assembled for that purpose." This does not limit God to express law only thru man, but other animals and vegetables. That being true, that is a part of our message which should be taught, you should accept, grasp, understand and practice.

But you say that making man into a law is one subject and making men healthy is another. You accept first and beg second. If you will consider that source is the same and from source's viewpoint health is law and law is health, hence health and law are one, why divide them, accept one and eject other—a condition as impossible as to contradict drawing of water into clouds when sun shines. You could admit sun shines and deny drawing of moisture, yet it is in spite of opposition.

If same man has no subluxations, and his Innate Intelligence is free to act thruout his body, THEN THAT MAN PERSONIFIES MORALS in any and every viewpoint; because source of his innate is fountain head of morality, and nothing can be greater in morality than infinitude.

God is good, God is sincere, doing right thing, at right time, under right circumstances in right place. All morals are sunbeams from itself. Ten commandments are personifications of Innate's intents as personified in men and women. But that moral part of this message we should teach, and you accept, practice and preach. Probabilities are you would offer rebuttal on ground that this is taught at your church, that you did not come to a "medical college" to learn law or religions.

We assume your mind, so far, stands as follows on this last idea.

"With health question we agree except that you have gone too far. It's consistent to adjust man to get him well, but when you introduce the God attribute we disagree. With law phase, we leave that to 'law makers' who are elected and they know what is best and right. Our purpose in coming to a Chiropractic school has nothing to do with their squabbles and disputes. As to religious viewpoint, we could not countenance your preachings. They oppose all we know or have known; what we have been taught or desire to know along these lines. We are satisfied with our spirituality as it is."

Our reply, in brief:—We study MAN. We make no claims to be a student of religions, statutes or medicine. We have not studied this or other worlds' clouds or bowels of earth. We have never been off this planet and don't propose to until it comes our time, then we'll go willingly. But, we do claim to be a student of man and theological, law, or health questions with which he comes in direct or indirect contact—they have a bearing on his condition. All man may think, do or sense—that he can give or receive, comes prominently within our sphere of study.

There is but one man, he has one source and one body. At no time or place can we disconnect any material part from any other material part, or satisfactorily disassociate any immaterial part from any other immaterial part without disintegration taking place to the part separated.

His soul, spirit (or what other title used) is ONE, no more, no less. As his body (1) cannot be separated from its other parts, neither (2) can its Innate be separated from its various attributes neither (3) can material be separated from its immaterial—they are separate and yet one entity. They are one and must be studied as such. As we cannot draw dividing lines between hand and wrist, neither can we make division and say here one ends and another begins; body and soul are one…

---

v. 26 1952 Conflicts Clarify (pp.40-41)

When physician operates, he does so to allow material "Nature" to cure or heal. When face to face with "What is 'Nature'?" he will reply it is a name given to sum total of sympathetic reflex action which is product of physical properties, therefore physician does not need assistance of God or Innate in any of his work.

Approach Chiropractor and he will say, "We know there is a creative intelligence; it had sufficient power to create the world, build you, and put you in it. It still continues to govern the world and its planets in all actions. Each movement we express is controlled and guided by that same intelligent power. It is individualized in each vegetable, animal, or human being. You may name this universality God. It is this individuality which we credit for our existence and it works unhindered in normal man, and restricted in expression in the sick.

Chiropractor liberates passages and sees that Innate Intelligence (individual God) performs thon's duties. Chiropractor studies this intellectual Innate power and how it works in unison with every action performed. If man be at ease, normal, then he cannot be at dis-ease with his Creator, himself, or his neighbor...

Behind all function is an intelligence which determines what character it shall take; how much or quality it shall be which segregates its divisions and places cells of proper consistency, etc. Many call it God, others soul; subconscious, non-conscious, or unconscious mind; instinct, intuition, or the term we prefer— Innate Intelligence. Innate—born with; Intelligence—intellectual power.

To Palmer, God is more than just the intelligence of the universe it is the actual living soul animating the human body. The soul is at once the sunbeam and the doorway. It is a drop from the ocean and the ocean. He referred to God by the non-gender "Thon."

With this extensive look at God in the context of B.J.'s quest for the inner wisdom, we are better prepared for his views on religion. This will fill the next few chapters.

Part III
On Religion

Palmer's view of religion is articulate and unique. He blends a pantheistic insight into God's immanence with a stress on the reality of direct revelation, while maintaining a scientific worldview that any religion should have practical proof rather than faith and belief, while all the time acknowledging that every religion is based on the same basic experience which has its roots in the fact that every human has the same innate intelligence.

Symbols of Chiropractic

PSC assembly 1916

48

Chapter 6
On Chiropractic as Religion

In these writings, we can see that B.J.'s understanding of religion had to do with the expression of God in living man. This will be discussed in more detail in future chapters. To B.J. religion should be based on the expression of health in the body, the ability of the educated mind to commune with the innate. The intelligence that materializes through matter is to him, the source of all religions and by adjusting the subluxation, the chiropractor allows that source to shine through.

---

v. 22 The Bigness of the Fellow Within (pp. 65)

Chiropractic is not a religion in the ordinary, accepted, and usual under-standing of that term as religions exist now and have existed for centuries and are established in the minds of human conduct.

The principles and practices of Chiropractic cannot be made into a religion. Religions have rituals and robes, ceremonies and conditions which create ministers who perform marriages, conduct funeral services, have a heaven for good conduct and a hell for sinners, who can pray away sins for a fee and save souls that go haywire.

Religions have saviors, apostles, and a Koran or Bible, establishing an intermediary between man according to the particular kind of GOD in which that religion believes. They create abstract language which is to be taken as texts, repeated and interpreted by preachers who preach and cannot practice what they preach because nothing they preach is subject to proof because they are based on what they "believe" and "have faith" in. All religions have well defined and established concepts around which they wrap the necessity of begging for their existence to perpetuate themselves.

Chiropractic, in principle and practice, has none of the above. It has no pulpits or steeples; its "dogma" is the Innate Intelligence within every living quadruped or biped and can be practiced anywhere there is a vertebral *subluxation*.

Chiropractic has no Sunday or Sunday school; no one day set aside to worship the deity on bended knee while looking downward to the supposed abode of a theoretical devil. It is applicable any day of the week wherever there is a sick being.

Chiropractic has no Lord's prayer to repeat; no ten commandments or hymns to sing. Chiropractic has a positive knowledge of when and where there is a vertebral subluxation which he knows how to correct, well knowing that the Innate within is all sufficient to restore absent function. Chiropractic establishes no mental or verbal mental standard to stimulate an artificial increase of a Universal Intelligence, of an Innate Intelligence, or inhibit the inhibitions of a supposed-to-exist satan. Chiropractic has no deity to which we can direct instructions of how to run the universe, or a soul to save for heaven or from hell. Praise or fear has no place in our logic or reasons why or how to live a normal healthy life.

---

v. 24 1950 Fight to Climb (pp. 492-3)

The Story of
IS CHIROPRACTIC A RELIGION?
At one time, in early history of the development of Chiropractic philosophy, D. D. Palmer contemplated building his Chiropractic philosophy into a religion. He was not a student of an orthodox creed, sect, or denomination, notwithstanding he had studied many thoroly. He was like Abraham Lincoln, in that he knew there was a Superior Intelligence that governed all things, including bipeds and quadrupeds. He believed that no sect, creed, or denomination incorporated anything practical in its application to man.

Chiropractic today, to many who have dug into its reality and application, does what all creeds, sects, and denominations preach about, wish they could do, try to do, viz., unite God into man, and physical man in tune with abstract God.

Of late, there has been a tendency of some of our best students to link or edge in a creed religious philosophy into the Chiropractic practice. Somewhere there IS a demonstrable and practical

50

application of truths that underlie all religions. Somewhere there is a stability of fact weaving itself in and thru this earnest desire of men. If any fact IS, then there is a practical explanation....

---

v. 24 1950 Fight To Climb (pp. 541)

Chiropractic, per se, is evolutionary and revolutionary to medicine. If its truths unfold a new and better concept of relationship between cause and effect, creator and created, and these clearly walk boldly into religious fields, then let responsibility fall where it of right belongs, viz., to religion for not having correctly interpreted true relation TO man THRU man and his health welfare.

This is not the fault of Chiropractic or D. D. Palmer who discovered this hitherto mysterious impractical relation of God to man, and man to God.

Notwithstanding all religions go thru minor evolutions, fundamental behind all NEVER changes, is stable, true, and that is LAW itself. Only man's understanding of what man thinks, speaks, writes, and prints about man's views goes thru change.

Some readers may think this story closely allied to pantheistic religion; that we try to associate man's life and his health akin to that relationship. Even if we would, we could not do better than has been done before. We ARE the living expression of all sound religions, based on same fundamental, regardless of creed, sect, or denomination. LIFE IS LIVING RELIGION of ALL religions.

We could not, even tho we wished, disassociate one from other. All one can do is to attempt to take religions out of theory and impracticability and make them scientifically sound and practically applicable. It is impossible to discuss any involved subject containing as many elements as this, without discussing ALL elements, AS they apply. From time to time, we have interjections by way of explanation as to WHY and HOW we introduce and use the matter under discussion. This is done to prevent misconception and to clarify understanding.

v. 26 1951 Conflicts Clarify (pp. 166)

From a letter to Marcus Bach:

We assume you have read our writings and know whereof WE speak. If you can imagine the derision, contempt, scoffing he presents in trying to make it appear that we are establishing an unfounded, ungrounded, fantastical religious "cult", then you know what we are opposing. No where in any of my writings will you find anything taking on any appearance of a religion, other than to acknowledge as fundamental a Universal Intelligence, call it God if one must, which is personified in man as a Unital Innate Intelligence; one of which is all intelligence, all powerful sufficient for the Universe, the other of which is all intelligent and all powerful sufficient unto the unit, be that unit man or animal, insect or tree, etc., as exemplified in any, every, and all LIVING objects…

---

v. 23 1950 Up From Below (pp. 337-44)

Excerpts from "The Story of the Lord's Work"

Chiropractor does not go thru red tape "repenting and coming to Jesus" (when he already belongs to God, good or bad), about having "soul or spirit brought to Jesus," to get persons to clinics. You, as a Chiropractor, would not go thru those misinterpretations of ideas to get patients to come to you to get well. Chiropractor recognizes same necessity as any church. Poor man, criminal, prostitute, sick person lies in bed, dying. Chiropractic recognizes necessity of sickness as much as it does that of criminals and poorness; yet we recognize necessity AND CAUSE. We know why man is poor, why another is a criminal, why man is sick in bed, why other man is a drunkard. Rather than alleviate conditions, we adjust cause of unit which makes them so. For every condition for which church exists, Chiropractor will show a unital cause for same condition. We know how to adjust, and proceed to do so in conformity with laws of God, or Lord, or other name you see fit to call it. We recognize universality of law as much as any minister—perhaps more—but we also recognize *a cause* which he does not

52

because his ideas of poorness, criminology, sickness, drunkenness, have been given to him by superstitious set of men. He recognizes a necessity but does not know connecting link between mission of church and cause behind necessity. Church man recognizes sickness and believes in faith and prayer; medical man believes in faith and pills. Both have seen same disease, but each has a different way to treat same symptoms.

Chiropractor sees no symptoms, doesn't care about them, pays no attention to prayers, pills, or faith, but finds cause and adjusts it. Minister has two links; Chiropractor has the third. As Chiropractors, we recognize our duty to be adjusters of the CAUSE of sickness, drunkenness, and poorness. We have connecting link between God and man—that knowledge of cause supplies necessity.

Look to every religion. Laws of Mohammed, Buddha, Confucius, Good Spirit of Indians, Pope of Roman Catholic Church, Czar of Greek Orthodox Church, and Christ of Christian era— universal recognition of universal God. We recognize no difference between because all look at same thing and same world thru a present or once mortal man. Mohammed, Buddha, Confucius, Pope, Czar, and Christ are all people who lived or are living. A person who believes in Confucius watches a tree or man grow and says, "Confucius does this." We watch trees and men anywhere and ALL grow according to God-like laws. Each man interprets this differently, and interpretation takes a different name, and he is different religiously. After all, it is a repetition of what has gone before, except that now we assume different men came to save us than existed before. What have any blank repeaters added to onward movement of world? Where have they added anything more than necessity and church? Have they added a cause?

No—they leave that for the doctor; it is within his province. Inasmuch as God made the world, it seems hard to draw lines between what was and what was not. Minister should be minister and doctor at same time, as olden priests were. Chiropractor adds third or unknown quantity— the cause. By so doing, he re-establishes religions from another viewpoint. Much that has gone before will cease; theory will be replaced by facts; superstition will

53

be replaced by art and science, and much howling and praying will be replaced by reasonable philosophy.

Analyze man's circumstances more practically. He hasn't a cent. Has nothing in his stomach—face shows it. Has rags on his body, looks rough, poor in every sense, because he has no strength with which to work. He says, "If I could get a job, I would go to work." He has not right currents going to his brain, or enough of them to hold a job. He is poor in cash and endeavor because he is poor in currents. He is poor in action because he is poor in thot; poor in thot because he has a poorly functioning brain to think with. He might be called lazy, but that proves lack of currents in his brain. He is poor because there is a cause. Laziness is a disease as much as insanity. We have seen laziness adjusted and case became most ambitious of men

There is a cause. Treating effects with prayers, Bibles, or soft soap talk does not help. They need what we have in Chiropractic. Give to life of prostitute vertebral adjustment, and without anything else, without uplifting thots of any character, that individual will become and live life of a moralist, not a "Christian" to the commonly accepted term. When that woman gets right function coursing thru her body, she cannot live wrong. Speeches, talks, or sudden conversions do not adjust causes....

Nature furnishes enough mystery—why make more with dogmas as regards the incomprehensible?

The divine ray in traversing the obscure chambers of the brain is decomposed into three ideas: justice, truth, and duty. Endeavor of man, divine function of freedom from disease, end of life is to establish on earth in the form of actual works three ideals: to strive that the beautiful, dutiful, just, be made flesh.

... Religions, builded upon treating effects, will no sooner go down to be replaced with adjustment of causes, than medicine. Conditions of therapeutics and religions are same; applications somewhat different; but as much can be said for various means of therapeutics as well as various forms and kinds of dogmas.

Chiropractic, tho, makes one complete change—it contradicts theories of medicine and religions and replaces them with facts.

Whether or not you admit it, we are laying a fundamental of what could be plain because it is not a question of faith or belief. We KNOW there is a God. We know there is a Universal Intelligence and a Lord, because we think with bodies that prove it a reality. We deal with fundamental law of cause and effect rather than effect for effect. Consequently, as we have, so we are, so will we overturn therapeutical ideas. Not today or ten years from now, but time will come when the fundamental you have will be the new religion. It will be religion of all nations, because all nations have spines, live thru lives of torment and pain, and they are going to be adjusted and get well. Trend of modern thot is Chiropracticward.

These writings on religion make it obvious that chiropractic is envisioned as an advance on human history. This view that religions of previous ages were lacking a perspective of science and thus, much of the truth that should pervade religion is an advance in consciousness. This will be discussed in the Epilogue.

Chapter 7
On Religion In General

It is important to distinguish the difference in Palmer's writings about religion. Above, was his explicit discussion of whether or not chiropractic is a religion? In this chapter, we have a related discussion, but it is broader. It discusses religion as a phenomenon, but always relates it back to the central questions of God in the creation. This is also the beginning of Palmer's questioning of humanity's search for answers. Why is there a need to create religion?

He was greatly influenced by Frazer's *Golden Bough*. This chapter begins with B.J. discussing Frazer's views on religion as it relates to Thailand. This piece was originally written during Palmer's trip in 1933 to Asia. It was rewritten and published in 1953. Thus, it falls within the confines of the period from which this book is derived. This quote is very important because it shows how B.J. looks at history, and how he analyzed Frazer from a developmental perspective. He describes science as the "Handmaid of Religion."

The other religions that Palmer discusses in detail are Buddhism and Hinduism. I have not included any of these writings in this volume. Most everything that he wrote on these subjects was more encyclopedic. There *are* several areas where he comments extensively on these religions. His writings on Buddhism will be discussed in the Epilogue along with a more extensive look at his comments on Frazer.

The rest of this chapter will look at Palmer's view of religion as perennial, whereas, all religions to him are basically the same because they seek to answer the same questions.

---

v. 29 1953 Upside Down and Right Side Up (pp. 690-2)

We would rather a wider sweep, and define religion as "a conception formed by man of the nature of the Universe of which he is part, of the Power responsible for and governing it, and of his relation towards that Power." This statement contains, we think, all that is implied in Sir James's definition, but it includes more besides. In his definition Sir James seems to imply something static in form of religion as adopted by mankind, but, as History teaches us, this is not so, and definition given above would not in any sense imply such a state; on contrary, it would make of religion a dynamic

56

force, one of which the conception varied from age to age and among all types of men, according to their stage of development, moral and intellectual.

Moreover, it would at once place relation of science to religion upon a different plane. Sir James writes as if he considers Science an end in itself, but we cannot look upon it as such. He speaks of science assuming that course of nature is governed by operation of immutable laws acting mechanically. So is working of an engine. Even so, no one, scientist or layman, would assume that engine made itself, or just happened. Somebody must have made engine, before it could be governed by any laws. In same way we hold it to be an entirely rational view, from a scientific standpoint, to assume that some Power which, for argument's sake, we call God, made the Universe before it could be governed by any laws, whether immutable or variable; and that Power that made the Universe probably made laws as well.

Scientists themselves have to assume hypotheses, and if this view were only acceptable to scientists, it would help to clear the somewhat heated and cloudy atmosphere which still hides religion and science from one another, and raise work of science, as we have said, to a much more lofty plane without in any way impairing its value. We hold that science, which seeks truth in Nature, and religion, which seeks truth in God, cannot conflict, since Nature is the work of God, and therefore more we learn of Nature, nearer we approach God.

Science can never be an end in itself—it must be a means to an end, and highest imaginable; and scientists, who kept this end in view and never allowed their work to obscure it from vision, would not become, as some still do, so lost to real meaning of life, and so remote from hearts and yearnings of men. Science is, indeed, Handmaid of Religion.

We feel the difficulty between Science and Religion rests upon fallacious conception that Religion must necessarily be static. True religion is nothing of the kind, and one of greatest stumbling-blocks of this age, this highly intellectual and pragmatic age, is to think religion still rests either upon forms, or dogmas, or even upon names and Persons. Buddhism is 2,500 years old; Christianity is 1,900; and Mohammedanism is 1,300. What are these spans of years in life of man? Gautama, the Buddha, calculated 5,000 years as limit of duration of his religion. He was wise. There is a popular saying in Siam that at the end of the 5,000 years the Buddhist priest will have left to him only a small piece of yellow cloth resting on his ear!

Who can imagine or conjure beliefs of man in another 2,500 years? Religion was made for man, not man for religion; and man conceives his religion in accordance with his stage of development. It is a common saying that "God made man in His Own Image." A friend once put forward the converse, "Man made God in his own image," as probably more correct, since idea itself is, must be, entirely man's. But in 2,500 years this Universe will still be here and Power governing it, and in all probability man will still be here. Let him then, with reverence, continue to probe marvelous mysteries before and around him in Nature, and keep steadfastly his aim in view, to approach nearer to the Power.

---

v. 24 1950 Fight To Climb (pp. 534)

As far back as records go, human beings have organized themselves into groups to worship at the feet of the Great Unknown. It might have been nature worship; phallic worship; perhaps worship to Buddha, Mohammet, or Christ. Each group said and did those things in those ways which came best within their understanding.

Today we think we know more and better how and which is right and wrong, than previous generations. Time brings forth new sects, creeds, or denominations, each with a new savior, each contending all others wrong, his alone right.

They did not know; we do! Backing up to dark ages when little, if anything, was known, Law worked, building human races, running worlds, as efficiently then as now. People were born, lived, and died, no better or worse then than now.

Nothing any organized group did then, or has said since, has changed any part or parcel of that law. People are born, live, and die today the same as then. That should be obvious to any person. It was not vital then, nor is it vital now, that we think as we did or do. It IS vital that LAW makes no difference in what MAN thinks.

What Is "Religion"?

"Religion" is vague and seldom defined, yet generally understood by all. We define it two ways:

1st. "Religion" is a single, simple understanding of an association of a universal and unital abstract law which has builded natural composite units thru which to express itself. It is everywhere where the naturally builded unit is, because it is within that unit.

2nd. To vast majority, religion is found only in written, printed, or expressed word of others, each to his own authority; is a dress parade found only in certain edifices subscribed for and erected to that specific purpose, where tribute is paid to sustain ordained and educated authorities; is gloriously robed; is outwardly supported by endless complexed manifestations; is found in certain periods of week and hours in that certain edifice, wherein parishioner humbles himself in prayer and supplication to his deity thru certain rituals and ceremonies without which he loses his soul; saving his soul by mumbling certain definite, fixed rotations of certain words which he memorizes and repeats without end, and in which the temple in which he or she lives is a vivid demonstration of violations of every precept in his every concept…

---

v. 28 1952 Answers (pp. 86)

RELIGIOUS CONCEPTS

ALL religions are based on some concept of a Jehovah, God, Great Spirit, or Universal Intelligence. Human beings are based on their beliefs and faiths in a Supreme Being that springs matter into life, action, function, and motion, expressing material manifestation of that factual reality.

v. 28 1952 Answers (pp. 86-7)

THEY ARE THE SAME

Regardless of whether it be Hottentot, Kaffir, Balinese, Esquimeaux; ignorant or intelligent; barbarian or civilized; ancient days or now—all conceived some greater power than that which we educationally possessed to which they looked for guidance, help, and to which they prayed for better things, thanking the giver for all received, little realising whom they acknowledged as their Savior, if any; or whether he denied any or all; or whether the supplicant was so ignorant he didn't care; or even if he be agnostic, atheist or infidel— he would get the same internal health as one who believed everything and had faith in all.

Same health would be restored to a Buddhist, Mohammedan, Confusionist, Hindu, or whatever other religion he professed or denied. Out of all this, the native viewpoint, was a "primitive" worship of natural procreation and what such meant as the source of all life, which was their simple understanding of the birth and beginning of all things— sex—hence "phallic worship." (See THE STORY OF PHALLIC WORSHIP, Vol. XXII, p. 514, 1949, Palmer.)

As man left the natural and normal, common to all mankind, he built artificial lives, as he educationally thot of creation, heaven, hell, purgatory, etc., rather than the internal Innate life within himself as it was, and builded variously construed "educated" ones, creating educated understandings of Gods of varying degrees of comprehension, building religions of educated designs, making God more man-like.

---

v. 28 1952 Answers (pp. 91-92)

What is IT which causes mankind to think of "God" (or some other name) that rules him Sunday, and makes him think that God is a "cult" when he reasons that so long as God rules the world and man is a part of that world, it also governs him? What is IT which flows INTO man from God, THRU MAN from brain to body, which causes action, motion, function, which makes preachers

60

revere such and scientists deny such? What is that peculiar quirp in some men who admit the factual God on Sunday, and call IT a fantastic hallucination in himself the balance of week? How can man differ so widely on the fundamental always-present, always-obvious, internal intelligence within himself, that one man can confirm one day of the week and other become negative on same subject other six days?

Why does man, in his conceited exalted education, confirm "God" as the Creator of all things Universal, and then call the same creative force in units such as reptiles, animals, fish, trees, and man, by that crude ignorant title of "Nature" which does this, that, and other things in units? Why does man seek to give highest type of Intelligence to a Universal force and give it the lowest type of ignorance—such as reflex action or sympathy from the solar plexus center—in man? Why does he seek to belittle that which is the same in the universe as is found in units such as man?

v. 28 1951 Answers (pp. 414)

People who set themselves up as authorities about God are prisoners in primitive concepts. Their educations are confined in dungeons of obsolete-fear-theology.

v. 34 1957 Evolution or Revolution? (pp. 82-3)

The conclusion we wish is that IT MAKES NO DIFFERENCE TO INNATE what he pins his faith in. As Marcus Bach has often said: "All roads that ARE GOOD lead to God," which is the Universal Intelligence, which is not influenced one second, in one or millions of units by the multitudes and throngs of worshipping conflicts. What we have said and explained so far is common to Chiro-practic and getting sick people well.

Involving foreign subjects, particularly religions, will be unpopular, denied, and denounced as outside our province, because of faith and belief they preach and pray to. In spite of criticisms, there are

61

people who seek facts and factual evidence as to whys and wherefores of life. These will understand! In spite of opposition, this much WE KNOW: ALL people are more or less sick and WANT TO GET WELL, relieved of aches and pains, long years of suffering. To THAT end they can affirm this NEW interpretation of this NEW principle and apply it to themselves. Beyond that, they will deny. However, if OUR construction IS SOUND, IT WON'T MAKE ANY DIFFERENCE...

B. J. (on right) with guide, Japan 1921

Chapter 8
On Medicine as Religion

As in many of Palmer's writings, the following passages sound quite similar. Please take note of the dates of each volume. When possible, I have placed quotes chronologically, thus giving some insight into the evolution of Palmer's thinking. Even though he mentions something in 1950, it may sound like he is repeating the same thing in 1961, but please read on, because a period of ten years is very significant in the growth of an idea. As you will see in most instances, Palmer's ideas grow in depth and complexity as time passes.

Part of his writing style is to warm up with a theory that he has proposed before such as; MD's go to church on Sunday and deny the God in man the other six days. He usually uses such a statement as a springboard to discuss a new concept such as, "Disease is matter, cause is matter, cure is matter, all drugs are matter." Then he usually ends on a profound "high" note, such as, "We have observed, seen and studied THE ROAD WHICH HAS ALWAYS BEEN, IS NOW, IN EVERY LIVING CREATURE – BUILT BY THE LAW FOR IT TO TRAVEL OVER AND WITH. We looked at and saw the 'road' that was and is. We have merely interpreted THAT law 'road'." There is some method to his writing. I include similar quotes only when the new ideas propounded are worth the repetition.

Palmer does not directly call medicine a religion, although he does draw many parallels. Medicine acts as the intermediary between the body and innate intelligence. This is to Palmer, a type of sacrilege.

---

v. 23 1950 Up From Below The Bottom (pp. 3)

Medically, there is no Innate Intelligence because it is not a materiality subject to being weighed, measured, or proven as a given quantity of matter. It cannot be seen under microscope, poured into a retort, or given chemical analysis. It is not provable in length, height, pounds, or gallons. It is an ABSTRACT quality, but as such it IS subject to an ABSTRACT quantity measurement as it flows THRU a material agency.

If nothing exists to medical mind except as it can be physically proven in the lab, how about God? Yet he professes to "believe" that. Physiologists explain away all anatomical and physiological vari-ables AND constants as "sympathy"—"by means unknown", thru a "sympathetic nervous system", later called an "autonomic nervous system", for that is far away from and as close to saying IT is "automatic" and still fight shy of acknowledging there could be or is an Innate Intelligence that is not matter....

And still there are those who direct lives and health of our people who say there is no Supreme Intelligence that governs the universe; there is no Innate Intelligence in man, which is SO great, SO wise, SO intelligent that it has directed, created, and controlled all mankind, is doing so today and will continue tomorrow. The Chiropractor should study Innate as a factor in getting sick people well!

---

v. 23 1950 Up From Below (pp. 216-7)

This attitude of "science" of medicine reminds me of M.D. who goes to church Sunday morning. He prays with a vim and a spirit to "the Almighty, Great, Good, Omnipotent God; All-wise God who made the earth in six days; separated the waters from the land; put fish in one, and birds, animals, and man on other; made man and then his improvement—woman. Great is the WISDOM of God to do all this"—yea, in church on Sunday morning. Change time and place to Sunday afternoon in a hospital. Same M.D. operates for appendicitis in one case; unsexes another woman; cuts out tonsils of another; removes a kidney in another, on Sunday P.M. Then he says: "Better send your children over and have their tonsils and appendix removed now, while young, so THEY won't have future trouble with them; they are useless organs."

This God-worshipper has been studying *physical* man four, eight, or ten years. He now begins to IMPROVE upon handiwork of God. Because this man has sat in a surgical pit for four years, he feels capable of saying—if actions speak louder than words —"God, you are ignorant. What do YOU know about making human beings? If you'd take a few lessons from surgeons, you'd make people according to OUR designs and leave our many 'useless' organs!" He makes a distinction between what he "believes" and gives money TO, and what he "knows" and takes money FOR. The former, his grandmother "believed"; the latter, his grandfather "did"; hence love-of-precedent is with him in both.

Peculiar? Sacrilegious? No. Just plain, every-day truths which you know but didn't know you knew because you'd never put that constructive-arrangement upon religious-surgeons before...

---

v. 23 1950 Up From Below (pp. 438)

You listen to sermon on "life" by minister who, if he gets sick, disputes "life" theory by having pills and quinine pumped into him under pretext that that "is life abundant." Education has its full swing. Each of three learned professions work hand-in-hand, each for itself yet for each other...

"Ye must be born again" . . literally a saying, scientifically a myth, philosophically a truth. Man need not be cast back into the melting pot of humanity, nor need he assume "a change of heart" paroxysmally or over night, but his perversions need rebuilding. His subluxations need adjusting, then he will fulfill conditions of foregoing, for he cannot do otherwise than live outline suggested.

---

v. 24 1950 Fight To Climb (pp. 697-8)

Medicine legally forces you to believe in pepsin, AS AN INTERMEDIATE, before you can get well. Legislation by police power with pressure insists you believe in statute, AS AN INTERMEDIATE, before you can get justice. Church by social ostracism demands you believe in Jesus, Mohammet, the Pope or Czar, AS AN INTERMEDIATE, before you can reach God. Don't misunderstand us to say we deny that there is no property in pepsin. It was good for fellow who made it. Same is true with statutes—they're good for those who framed and passed them; were so much spleen in his system that he used as a business to give vent to. Neither do we want you to understand that we deny divinity of Jesus, but we are condemning in no uncertain terms way mankind has twisted truth He uttered to way we dope it out today. Fault is not with Jesus, it's with people. Jesus prayed on highways—today you must go to church, pay a stipend for pew rent to do same act.

Education fixes standard and by education are you judged. Mass believing in medicine—then to deny its principle or application is to be condemned, by that standard…

Sickness, physician, medicine—physician and medicine intermediates. Innate, man, health—no intermediates. Sickness, crime, lawyer, statute—lawyer and statute intermediates. Sickness, immorality, Divine person, minister—divine person and preacher intermediates. Innate, man, morality—no intermediates.

God is in man—no need for physician, lawyer or minister. God is not in medicine, statute or a book. Physician, lawyer or minister are not needed more than are medicines, statutes or books. To listen to physician teach medicines, lawyer statutes, or minister the book does not assist God within to reach ourselves. Some Chiropractors do not preach God within ourselves—they preach what others say in a Book, doing which offers an obstruction—to adjust a cause is to let God within become God without, without advice or being asked to do so. Principle is same in all—no difference and all are wrong. God is source of health, law, divinity (if there is such) then to Thon must we go for it. Doctor, lawyer, preacher is an intermediate and not necessary. Health courses within us regardless of where we may be.

Same is true of law and spirituality—it is not necessary we go to doctor's office to take our pill, to court house to get justice, or to a church to pray, yet educational scale of today says we must or our endeavors are failures.

If we desire health it is within us, anywhere we may be; this is true of law and God. We can pray in cellar, garret, woods or prison— church and court house and doctor's offices are as much unnecessary intermediates as are officials themselves. Always looking to counsel of somebody else; to OUTSIDE forces, when only force that gives confidence, in times of trouble, is within. THE SAME PRINCIPLE still is. It was there long, long ago; it is with us today. Reformation!

---

v. 34 1955 Fame and Fortune (pp. 18)

Chapter III
ONE CONFLICT
Medical men admit God on Sunday, admit "nature cures" other six days, **in theory,** and deny BOTH seven days of week when THEY prescribe pills, powders, potions, prescriptions, and injections, thinking SUBSTANCE THINGS from **outside** "cure" something physically wrong **inside.**

Preachers of religions admit omnipresence, omnipotence, and omniscience of "The Kingdom of God is **within** you" from pulpit; preach this gospel with vehemence on Sunday; and when sick themselves, deny ability of internal God WITHIN man to get them well other six days of week, going to material medica materialists to have their material diseases therapeutically "healed" and "cured" by pills, powders, potions, prescriptions, and injections, thinking remedial things from OUTSIDE will cure something wrong INSIDE.

Medical men are in conflict between what THEY believe religiously and what THEY practice medically. Preachers are in conflict between what THEY preach religiously and what THEY do therapeutically when sick. There is NO consistency in principle or practice in either of their divided one-half dogmas or sciences. Medical men DENY there is an all-intellectual inseparable internal Innate Intelligence that gets sick people well. They ridicule Chiropractors who assert such is a factual actuality, calling our philosophy a "cult." Religious preachers assert there IS an all-external "God" that rules the universe, and DENY there is an internal God IN man.

Both medical men and preachers go to Chiropractors and get well because they permit the actual factual union of INNATE with THEIR PHYSICAL BODIES. Chiropractor has no such conflict. He KNOWS there IS an EXTERNAL Universal Intelligence and there IS ALSO an INTERNAL Innate Intelligence with which he cooperates, restoring one into and thru other.

---

v. 37 1961 The Glory of Going On (pp. 54)

M.D.'s, in and within themselves, each being a product OF a producer, medically lead a dual contradictory life. On SUNDAY, they go to church built of stone, on bended knee listen to preacher of what is called a religion, pray to the omniscient, omni-present, omnipotent "God" which created the earth, all its growing inhabitants, professing to be "God-fearing men"—ON SUNDAYS.

Then in the other six days they are the great scientific example of everything material. Disease **is matter,** cause **is matter,** cure **is matter,** all drugs **are matter.** In an offhand slip-of-the-tongue, the M.D. refers to "NATURE cures and heals," but HE does not know what THAT is. "Nature" is used to mask and blindfold HIS ignorance as well as to shield HIMSELF against ignorance of his followers. Doctor and patient, both are blind and deaf to everything surrounding and IN HIM AND THEM, but denying that ALL ETERNAL EXTERNAL YET INTIMATELY INTERNAL law which created him in the beginning, which runs him by day and by night; and to sarcastically call such a study a "cult", neither could such successfully deny its existence as a reality.

In our Chiropractic "philosophy", we have not devised, conceived, built, or manufactured ANOTHER "road." We have observed, seen, and studied THE ROAD WHICH HAS ALWAYS BEEN, IS NOW, IN EVERY LIVING CREATURE—BUILT BY THE LAW FOR IT TO TRAVEL OVER AND WITH. We looked at and saw the "road" that was and is. We have merely interpreted

68

THAT law "road." We have UNDERSTOOD THERE WAS SUCH, made it possible to correct interference **between** the law, per se, and its lack of expression IN the body...

B.J. in his garden watching the fish in the pool below

Chapter 9
On Christianity

This chapter goes to the heart of Palmer's burst of creativity from 1949-1952. These writings explain his view of Christianity, ministers, church, and organized religion in general. He is unabashedly frank as always.

In large part, Americans today don't go to church, consider themselves to be spiritual, are searching for answers in health and religion, and are overmedicated. Palmer offers an integral perspective that does not deny the spiritual and experiential truths of Christianity, but at the same time does not accept the traditional role of religion for modern man. It is for this reason, that I include much longer quotes in this section. The ideas are so complex, and the issues are so important, that I wanted the reader to get this straight from Palmer in his articulate and prophetic style.

---

v. 24 1950 Fight to Climb (38-40)

The history of man and of worlds is that of religious factions with frictions, with millions of murders committed in their various fair names. If religion is good—if wars are bad—why can't good get into man and eliminate the other?

As a youth, we found ourself in conflict with much that we heard, saw, and found practiced in churches. We went beyond people INTO METHODS used to reach people. They were too much churchianity and too little Christianity.

We went beyond methods used TO PRINCIPLES INVOLVED. We investigated religions of the world, past and present. We studied sects, creeds, and denominations.

We traveled into native haunts of religions. History is one monumental story of war after war, millions of men killing millions of men. Hatred has been and is everywhere prominent; intolerance is prevalent; jealousy between nations—therefore between its constituents—runs rampant. Yet EVERY religion teaches to defeat all that.

Religion, regardless of sect, creed, or denomination—is often accepted as a Sunday cloak; a script to be read; a creed to be followed closely on Sunday and loosely on Monday. Too often, religion is a pious, dressed-up state of Sunday mind, with a skin-em-to-the-bone state of Tuesday mind, justifying six days of cheat-'em by the oft-told alibi that "business is business." No greater epitome of language was ever said than "THE FATHERHOOD OF GOD AND THE BROTHERHOOD OF MAN." It is preached all around, seldom on, and very little of it is in use. We have A FATHERHOOD OF GOD, and man kills man when it comes to a BROTHERHOOD OF MAN against man.
Why should this be?

No one man or group of men has a private path to heaven or hell, or a special key to fit a private lock to the gates. That some ways seem better than others, after all, is a matter of geography and periods of world's history.

Man should better understand himself and his relationship of service to man and his duties while here in that relationship between man and his God; more than that is outside of the province of feeble man in the great scheme of things.

Religion should be an opportunity—regardless of what religion it is—to give man a better understanding of his place in the great scheme.

Man, however, often construes religion as an opportunity TO CREATE A SCHEME and FORCE all men to it, willy-nilly; and, if necessary, at point of sword, even to national murder, to bring it about. Religion, if it has any purpose to serve at all, is a rule of living, method of service between men and their places and duties in this world.

Average man who leads thinks THE WAY to lead is to super-stitiously become a super-visioned, high-powered dynamite-'em-into- heaven-or-hell fellow. Tendency of men, who become addicts of this religious game—is to go to seed, grow into ruts, narrow mentally in interpretations of their most holy responsibilities and duties they owe each other.

They grow serious—TOO damn serious. You rarely find any man who plants seed, harvests a crop, paves the road, and mentally broadens in his pointing the way. They lose human touch and become inhuman, dogmatic, and domineering. In action. Every man, some day and in some way, must find himself in this great religious question.

Sincere and honest KNOWLEDGE OF A GOD and a sincere, honest WORKING ABILITY to serve everything natural, finally became the sole approximate principle for which we lived; every waking hour of every day, to every man with whom we came in contact—not on the surface, but a living principle to which we sold ourself; not plastered on from without, but flowing freely from within; not holding ourself out as a leader, yet numberless young men have asked for counsel, that they might better be directed to find THEMselves.

We eventually found OUR salvation—but it wasn't within walls of average church building; nor was its wisdom spoken from mouths of average preacher. Religion, on the whole, is scrambled words which produce con-fusion, manufacturing misunderstanding, creating wars. No one preacher, sermon, or creed—but all of them—produce this.

God was the Common Denominator of all time—all people. WHY God could be sectarian; HOW God could be partial to one human color, or favor a special bit of geography; or close gates on all but thee and thou, failed to meet OUR concept of a just omnipotence.

There are no greater books than various Holy Bibles. IN SPITE OF sermons we heard, IN SPITE OF jumbled words they preached, IN SPITE OF ancient language they spoke—we still found PRINCIPLES enough within their covers good enough for everybody when humanely and humanly interpreted.

72

MAN'S RELIGION was manufactured of words and printed; but GOD'S RELIGION is hidden within PRINCIPLES incorporated between those words. Betwixt and between PRINCIPLES AND MEN were intermediary men. Intermediaries were not teaching so all who run could read. They mystified and made mysterious to us little worms on earth.

Churches were social organizations which catered rather than educated. Preachers were led by rings in noses, by men who paid for carpets, when they should be leaders of simple life and thot...

---

v. 24 1950 Fight to Climb (pp. 62-5)

B.J. commenting on the God Patient Chiropractor movement:

Many quotations of like character could be made. These are such as any Christian religious enthusiast would speak. That there IS a Law of the Universe, is obvious. That it IS per-sonified in man, in Innate Intelligence, is obvious. That a violation of the Unital Law means sickness, is obvious. That a correction of intermediate cause between Law and Expression will restore health, is obvious. To call this Law "God" is indicative of Christian interpretation of religion. There is Jehovah of Jews, Mohammet of Mohammedans, Buddha of Buddhists, Karma, Confucius, Hindus of India, Moslems of Bali, Phallic Worshippers of Bushmen of Australia, and Maori's of New Zealand, Great Spirit of our American Indians, etc., all of which are also religions.

Law of the Chiropractor IS SAME LAW to ALL religions. A vertebral subluxation in a Jew, Mohammedan, Buddhist, Confucionist, is SAME violation of one UNIVERSAL law to ALL mankind, regardless of what he interprets educationally as right road to heaven or royal road to hell. Chiropractor DOES recognize a Universal Law, universal to ALL people regardless of whether he believes in voodoo, is savage, lives in jungle or city. There is no one CHRISTIAN GOD for all mankind, regardless. I find no fault in G-P-C movement adhering closely to advocacy of THE Law, but I find it taking on aspect of a CHRISTIAN GOD, thus excluding broad principle that Chiropractic principle and practice applies with equal force to ALL people of world, regardless of sect, creed, country, or color.

D. D. Palmer followed no sect, creed, or denomination. If he leaned to any, it was to principle of spiritualism, and then only to its religious aspect. Did he ever intend to make a religion out of Chiropractic? That depends upon what constitutes a religion. If, by "religion" is meant setting up one particular savior of souls of mankind, such as Christ, then this was not his idea of his service to sick mankind. If, by religion, is meant establishment of a church, of a one-day-of-the-week Sunday, with a ritual of hymns, sermons, robes, preachers, etc., this also was repugnant to his concept of universality of Chiropractic vertebral subluxation and its adjustment. If, by religion, is meant that sins, souls, saviors, to save them, need be established, then that was revolting to his idea that anybody anywhere could get sick and get well whether sick person believed in any, all, or none of them…

What kind of a religion would he have established? We are convinced it would have been like the Bahai Movement where ALL men are equal. He would have set no creed, sect, denomination, church, preacher. He would have established TEACHERS OF A KNOWLEDGE OF LAW AND ITS APPLICATION TO SICK MAN.

---

v. 24 1950 Fight to Climb (pp. 643-4)

THE CAUSE AND CURE OF MOOTED ISSUES
10. AUXILIARY RELIGIOUS PROBLEM.

We shall speak particularly to Christian religion, altho others should get consideration. One is as important as another. Everywhere is a paradox. It would be a peculiar world if it were otherwise. We do everything backwards; we desire to go forward, and walk downhill. We build ourselves a skiff and head it straight for middle of ocean.

Educated physician, religiously taught, appeals to Jesus in spirit, but denies God in body. Surgeon goes to church in morning and prays

74

to Jesus, then in afternoon retires to hospital to cut out an appendix. Where is God in that body or in that butcher's mind? Man builds false gods, constructs idols, builds mansions of churches, erects crucifixes of gold, then educationally writes about a Savior who came to reconcile man to God.

Man theoretically looks for God in everything but in the object where Thon is. Thon is *in* man; man was made by Thon; yet we deny him there and build special places where we expect him to be when we go there; manufacture specially designed images upon and thru which we can hypnotize our minds to believe that if we pray to them we will be saved by this Savior.

At present there are approximately 280 religions in the U. S., each with special viewpoint of what kind of cross on steeple draws special favors of Christ; or which special Leader can do most for them in heaven. They do not agree on Bible from which to teach or study.

They come and go and change every year. Religions are multiplying and dying, and more will come in future. Which one is right? Are all right? In religions there is a conflict. Of theology, there is but one God, and to this all religious students commonly agree. Purpose of theology is to draw man nearer to God, say some. Under present solution, it is to make God more manifest in man. But all this is subservient to an organized, commercialized religion to build costly buildings, altars, robes, etc.

Let us study contrast.
Here is a religion with followers, each paying money to a minister to build a church, buy an altar of gold, robes of silk, etc. After each religion is established, they vie with each other to see who get most members and introduce best music to draw people from one assemblage to other. Rivalry is at hand.

Here is a theology. It is a direct question of communication between God and man, man to his God. All men may get close *to* God. It costs nothing to get into contact with God. They need not nail two sticks together in any definite form to notify God where they are stopping in woods, for fear God will get lost therein.

75

Imagine millions of dollars stored up in useless timbers, bricks, gold, robes, steeples in every state, for churches, salaries, maintenance, etc. Think of millions more of useless property standing idle six days a week, which is not paying taxes to help support balance of town. Think of millions of missionaries who go to a foreign country to get them to repeat *our* prayers, to put *our* theory against their centuries-old method of worshipping. Who is to say which is best? Think of waste that goes into religions, when theology could and would make it unnecessary to treat soul diseases of brain thru mental manifestations.

God is not within covers of a book. God is a law, yet unwritten, open to every unit to study, interpret, and observe to his satisfaction. God made the unit, gave it life, and continues to supply it from birth to death; in fact, Life is God and God is Life.

God enters man's brain exactly as does "electricity" first enter dynamo before it gets into wire to reach motor or globes, etc. When that flow of God *is from inside outward to all the rest of that man's body,* it is normal to that unit, that man is a disciple of God because he receives message *direct,* lets it flow to where it belongs, and does that which message requires.

Man is born with God within him; it is the real Thon and is never separate except in death, and then only in relevancy. To maintain any other kind of a system of worship seems a misinterpretation of Source and but a play of treatments on effects which we want modified and don't know how to go about getting it.

If man were normal, healthy, all parts in relation with all other parts, brain in touch with all its body, God-like mind in touch with all its functions, religions would never have been needed. They were born out of pathology; they thrive with pathology and breed in ratio as pathology exists. He who is sick needs a mental crutch. He who is independent needs less of such.

Adjustment makes more of God perceptible in man's education. Hence, as one receives other improves; as one gets well it approaches its Source, hence needs less abnormal support from preconceived education born out of it.

76

Chiropractor does not make more God, in brain or body. He merely adjusts subluxation, adjusts relationship between where God is in man to where it isn't in same being; gives God full play in activity. Only practical solution of this problem is that man is made more normal; Thon takes care of itself. We need reach that exalted stage of average animal that is not under domestication. No man can be his brother's keeper; neither can any Savior act as an intermediary or go-between for himself and another Source. To help man help himself, to adjust him that he may adjust himself, to be his friend, is sufficient.

---

v. 27 1952 History Repeats (pp. 738)

There is a distinction between church-believer in Christ and Christian—believer in God. Paradox shows there is a wide range between churchianity and Christianity.

B.J. at the Olive Tree in the Garden of Gethsemane 1925

Chapter 10
On Jesus

These writings on Jesus speak for themselves. For the 1950's, Palmer was way beyond mainstream thought. He refused to admit anything that was supernatural. From healing to the virgin birth, Palmer was very clear; the rule of natural law was miraculous enough.

v. 23 1950 UP From Bellow (pp. 17)

We believe in the *legitimate* birth of Christ.
To have it otherwise is to condemn Mary and upset all embryological knowledge and law of births, AND LAW IS GOD.

Law, to be eternal, fixed, and a constant, must always be the same. It can't change to meet accidents or theories of life or religions. Must we be an infidel, agnostic, or atheist because we desire to legitimatize the birth of a great man—make his coming in accordance with law, rather than denying it?

We don't believe any religion the right one, as all are intolerant of others. Christ was tolerant, even unto enemies.

All religions are good because all have a common purpose. We belong to one church—the church of God. The walls are everywhere— Thon's presence is always everywhere. Should we, then, be condemned unheard because we attend no church, follow no particular sect or creed, so long as we uphold the God work?

v. 24 1950 Fight To Climb (697-8)

System under which every organized and systematized religion is conducted IS THRU THAT OF AN INTERMEDIATE. You pray to Jesus, and yet no where did Jesus hold himself up as an example—he said "Honor thy Father," referring to God. He taught us to appreciate God. He was but a man trying to teach. This same viewpoint is true of all theologies. Lodges recognize God. For that reason lodges follow a truer religion than churches; one omits intermediate and takes you direct to source, the other makes you believe in divinity of an intermediate before you can reach cause.

v. 24 1950 Fight To Climb (pp. 106)

A man once came, saw, heard, thot, and preached a better way to be saved.

He went to the Mount of Olives to pray. He was kissed—and betrayed. He was crucified.

FOGS OF PREJUDICE AND DISBELIEF appeared and beclouded his way.

FOGS CAN'T LAST ALWAYS!

WE ARE SURROUNDED WITH LIGHT!

WE ARE BLINDED TO FACTS ABOUT US!

WE HAVE EYES AND SEE NOT WHERE TO GO!

WE SHALL SEE WHEN THE FOG RISES!

Historical fogs appear and disappear; visions appear and permanently remain; and Christianity is the result.

We have stood under that olive tree in Gethsemane.

We have walked the Via Dolorosa.

We have tarried by each of fourteen stations, closed our eyes and felt His weighty burden.

v. 24 1950 Fight To Climb (pp. 703-4)

If Good Book is true, we read that "Jesus cured people." What disease does not matter. He must have done so in conjunction WITH law not opposing it. If He permitted a cure to occur by accidentally letting law act, then that is not science nor is it art. We hardly desire to concede that Jesus' acts were accidents, altho we have no proof they were otherwise. But we do believe people got well—therefore law was effective and accomplished its mission.

CONSTANT of life, health, morality and law is that God enters man in form of Innate Intelligence, passes thru spinal cord, ramifying to all parts of body in form of mental impulses. When they reach organs there will be health, law, moral abiding—that is our message. If that fact is true—and it is demonstrable—then the Chiropractor is working according to law when he adjusts subluxation.

And who is to gainsay that "the laying on of hands" was not done according to this now well known law of health? Who is to deny that Jesus did not do exactly that kind of work. We do not question statement of fact—we do tho think Good Book does not tell us all we should know about this subject. No blame can be fixed and, it's a question whether there is censure due. Men in those times were superstitious, they wrote what they remembered years after of things as they occurred.

Memory is defective, highly so when educated piffles with superstitions and myths. One whose life is based on such could not retain all of a demonstrated truth, his recitation thereof would be prejudiced and modified by previous educational memory As to spitting on mud for blindness, maybe and maybe not—if done, it could be accounted for same as a physician advised fresh air, sunlight and baths and gives a bread and water pill. Patient believes pill cured. If patient told about pill to second and third party and they eventually wrote chapters thereupon naturally fact is vice-twisted. If it is a fact that blind were made to see—so do we.

He got halt, lame, to walking normally—so does Chiropractor. He healed leper, so could we if given opportunity. And as to "raising Lazarus from the dead," we have known cases adjusted by Chiropractors having been given up to die and got well even to one case where in coffin eighteen hours and restored. (In using terms "He healed the leper," etc., we do so advisedly well knowing that even Jesus could not usurp His position as a man and do work of God. Neither can Chiropractor. He or we can but get man to a condition where law can work.)

Law is law—it is fixed, eternal, everlasting, stable—hence does not change because we do. Its thot is permanent, ours fluctuation, unstable, up today and down tomorrow. What is law today was same then. How far then can we agree that Jesus but did then what

80

we do today or vice versa? Is it inconsistent to assume that history repeats itself?

v. 23 1950 Up From Below (pp. 361)

The Christ as a sample character.
In this story we shall not discuss the Christ as a Divine Being, or as the Son of God.
We will admit it!
Each of us, as human beings, will profit more, as such, if we present the Christ as a human being, amongst human beings, as one mortal would associate with other mortal, as one who sacrificed as a human being to succeed as a human being, in his dealings with men and women as we, as students of human beings, would make a student of any other man, of his time or ours.

This view that Jesus was a man is mentioned again and again in book after book. As one who had found himself, one who had allowed innate to come from above down and from within out, and one who taught others how to do the same; also, one that was able to heal others with his hands. Palmer was at the very least, inspired by the life and teachings of Jesus.

Sea of Galilee 1925

Chapter 11
On Death and Reincarnation

Palmer not only extended his notion of Innate as the soul that leaves the body after death, but also, developed a detailed perspective on reincarnation. This was probably due to his studies of Eastern cultures, as well as his extensive travel around the world. Always, as the reader would expect, he brings these subjects back to the innate intelligence.

---

v. 22 1949 The Bigness of the Fellow Within (pp. 65)

If, as, and when man is separated from his Innate, *he is* dead, at which time the minister of the soul (Innate) says: "Here lies *the remains.*"

---

v. 23 1950 Up From Bellow (pp. 643-5)

The Story of
DEATH—OUR ATTITUDE TOWARD IT
Death—dissolution of Innate from matter. Sickness conditions made body untenable.
Death—theologically; philosophically.
Theology based on life { death }God.
When we die, it is "the will of God."
Theology is based on death { heaven / hell } eternal life.
Heaven—future life; hell—damnation.
Theology—"heaven and hell are places."
"your soul must go one place or the other."
By your conduct BEFORE DEATH is your place assured.
If you follow CUSTOM as ordained, you go to heaven; if not, then hell.
To which place you go, depends upon to whom you listen.
Turk ladies wear bloomers; men wear skirts.
In America, we reverse this.
Religions are the same: what is hell to them is heaven to us.
Interpretations of heaven and hell depend upon to what sect you listen.

Methodist—dancing
Baptist—tub of water
Negro Baptist—river
Unitarian—dance on Sunday, etc.
Classification of soul
spirit
intuition
subconscious,
etc.,
is not defined theologically other than in theory.
Death—dissolution of Innate from matter.
Diseased or accidental conditions make body untenable.
Subluxation made conditions.
Adjustment removes conditions.
Healthy conditions make body tenable.
Life, the insoluble.
Innate with matter.

Death occurs when *all* tissue cells are expanded; old age only possible philosophical DEATH. Innate leaves to again return to Universal Intelligence and again return to matter to advance and progress. "Death" is a condition; "life" is a condition; as is "disease" a condition of matter.

If we can stay conditions by adjustment, then well. "Heaven" and "hell" are educated conditions, not theological places. The soul, or Innate, is either normal or abnormal, according to fullness of its expression. Theologically, we weep, sorrow, mourn; say good things over thieves; waste money on flowers, expensive coffins, etc.; build steeples to God; go in debt for funerals, etc.; harbor sorrow for twelve months; spend money for prayers to save souls. Our actions belie things we profess to believe. Are we Christians? We would rather have a low standard and live it, than a high standard and deny it.

The modern funeral contradicts Christian teachings;
—special privileges with God to steer his soul to the straight and narrow path.
—have a minister save a murderer from going to hell on the scaffold.

All this smatters of theory, superstition, fables and myths—much like sympathy and reflex of medicine. When a flower dies, you bury it with a passing thot. Man is a flower; bury him likewise. Innate is greater than Educated; U.I. is greater than Innate, yet ignorant Educated implores, demands, pleads that U.I. do with Innate as Educated wants. U.I. KNOWS what to do with Innate; where to take it; where to replace it; how long to hold it. The Chiropractor will not attempt to dictate to his Superior. He takes facts as facts, thinks upon them accordingly, and acts. He will not weep because his greater self has gone to a better CONDITION—no sorrow, no crepe. The thief's Innate stands on a par with ours; its perversions were Educated.

We waste no great money on coffins, trimmings, funerals, etc. Innate is simpleness—the plainest possible. We will not cause ourselves to harbor sorrow for twelve months; no money will be spent to steer our Innate the way we Educateds think it should be steered.

We realize we are as close to God, Innately, as any man.
No theory, superstition, or myth will enter our thots or acts.
The Chiropractor will miss associations, but he will be glad a fulfilled life has reached a fuller stage. He will be filled with gladness. No flowers will be spent on the dead. Happiness will be his. A new and better life will be forthcoming.

Personally—incinerated within 24 hours
—no embalming
—no flowers
—no prayers
—no mourning
—no songs
"God Be With You Till We Meet Again." Our faults and good to be referred to at the service. We aimed to be a man of and for the people—to do them good. Theologically, death is nurtured by FEAR of the unknown future, therefore Educated "faith." Chiropractic philosophy teaches death and life are conditions. Our actions prove our KNOWLEDGE of facts of evolution and

84

reincarnation. Our knowledge is begotten of the proofs of Innate, therefore not open to theory.

---

v. 23 1950 Up From Bellow (pp. 323-6)

The Story of
REINCARNATION

We recognize certain facts, whether or not we wish to. There is one essential, that of life and death, as expressed thru matter, and cause and effect of life and death in creation. In observation of these there can be but ONE interpretation and that is of things as they are. If our eyes are open, vibrations are conveyed to them and vision is interpreted by the mind, whether or not we wish it. More we go into life and its requisites, we are forced to believe in reincarnation.

Whether or not we believe what we see depends upon how we interpret what is before us. Often you ponder on what "reincarnation" means. Interpretation generally given is not sufficiently broad to meet comprehension. Reincarnation is that state of condition wherein all intellectual power assumes and releases possession of bodies repeatedly in similar or varied forms at successive periods, for purpose of advancement, progress, benevolence, and justice of getting most out of least in future generations.

Reincarnation is a constant and persistent process, never ceasing when it takes possession or leaves—process works from time it leaves until it arrives and from time it arrives until it leaves. Reincarnation may be passing of our intelligence (at "death") to inhabiting brain of a cat, dog, or other animal in "next generation." First paragraph in Bible states, "And in the beginning God." Before there could have been anything, in definite form, by and thru senses of man, there was Intelligence—God. How far reincarnated intelligence could be compared with God is a question we can answer only comparatively.

Finite mind observes things in a limited way. If infinite mind talked frankly to a capable finite mind, we would learn much about

85

reincarnation and other branches of philosophy. In the beginning— God—an Intelligence. At that time we notice various composite forms of matter assuming shapes, accommodating adaptations, various habits and conveying various functions and being expressed thru them. From that period to this, there has been a constant transformation and transplantation of thot and matter— thot preceding its execution. This world, as well as many others, is governed by one intelligence thru composite schematic influences...

Then he loses identity and another corporeal and mental composite form takes place and carries progression one step further and is then obliterated; another comes; the general schematic arrangement assumes another advancement until century after century—aeon after aeon of time passes on.

The general world, as one unit, has progressed. In this sense, animals, vegetables, and man must use each portion of the schematic arrangement to act Universal Intelligence. It governs not only THIS EARTH but other worlds and their intelligences...

Earth rolls upon itself, thot reverberates upon its likeness—but every revolution was greater than one before. Reincarnation, then, is passing this Universal Intelligence thru various compositions, vegetable, animal, and human, and thru these media she can utilize concrete forms of things on earth and continually adapt it to circumstances, for ultimate purpose of making this world more highly productive.

We are not willing to concede all intelligence is totalized that it is dividualized into personal segments, yet we do not like to admit individuality of identities lingering thru time until proper and befitting media are found with which to take up work of some other unfinished form. Both of these hypotheses appear reasonable, i.e., if we judge character of thot thru its executing. Study musical geniuses, remarkable "phenomena" which manifest themselves in streaks in family. Again, how, from humble daily laborers, spring engineers, scientists, philosophers, and artists? How to account for facts as history records mankind is to soliloquize upon conditions preceding their present mental beings.

Often we are told that in space are existing those reincarnated souls set free, and that some day one will again be implanted in a human being. Perhaps this is so we cannot gainsay the assertion —be that as it may, we have enough to study in reincarnation if we take phases which are observable—past and present. From ameba to man (considered highest type of evolutionary form) it is often a fact that an individual is in communication with other souls which exist in space...

When we search for thots to express, we look to educated mind; but where does educated mind get them? From whence does Innate arrive? From a superior source—call it what you may. Man is in a constant evolutionary, progressive form physically and is constantly guided by a power greater and broader than his own. For Innate Intelligence to leave our body would be its death; yet there is still what you and we Innate Intelligence from the higher power, life would be of short duration—it is the constant interchange of knowledge between ourselves and a higher power which gives benefits of an association of material things; that is, thru sphere of reincarnation we receive experiences of natives of Africa, cattle in field, or other animals.

Some people evolutionize faster than others; not so much because creation in him is better or greater, but because he is a more receptive medium for purpose of receiving deductions of other congregations of thot gone before; because they have shut themselves off from connection with high powers. Again, other individuals who seem possessed with a superior ability along special lines constitute a cycle thru which higher intelligence is more constantly growing, producing equivalent of reincarnated action. If door is closed, action does not take place and brain becomes a worse medium to man and he does not progress.

Condition of matter equals ability of man to prove existence of a reincarnated life. Chiropractic is right because adjustments open mental windows and thot doors and the way for receptive power from a higher source, consequently means more definite action in brain cells and makes them capable of receiving superior power, hence receives more.

Do we believe in reincarnation? We are compelled to, because of what is manifested. It is not a question of belief or faith—it is seeing and knowing. Do we believe there will be a reincarnated existence? We observe a definite, specific action in people who live it—see them possessed of powers not attributes of the educated mind. We see them doing things, advancing thots and changes for which we can offer no other explanation.

China 1921

Chapter 12
On Innate and Educated or "We"

There was suddenly a change for B.J., he, the "I", the ego, expanded. Not in a pathological way as in egomania, but in a transformative way, as in enlightenment. There is ample evidence in the literature of the world's wisdom traditions, that the enlightenment process is a transegoic state of being which can become an embedded functional aspect to the personality. This transformation has been researched in many books and articles. It is generally agreed that it occurs in a series of stages, and often later in life. This may well be B.J. entering the first stage of a profound new structure of consciousness. He could no longer refer to himself without including his larger self, namely, the intelligence of the universe as personified in his corporeal form.

The first three excerpts below show how he described this change for his reader. Recognizing that it would be odd for the reader to come across the word "We" instead of "I." B.J. placed this Foreword in volumes 22-29. I have included the general preface, an addition to the foreword from 1952, and then at the beginning of volume 29, from 1953. This piece is very important, because it shows how profound Palmer's transformation was. He went back through an unpublished manuscript of over 1,700 pages that he had written in 1933 during his trip through South East Asia, and retyped the entire book to include "We" in 1953. After that is a famous chapter entitled, "The Dead Still Live," published in one of his last books, posthumously, in which B.J. described his awakening process.

---

v. 22 1949 The Bigness of the Fellow Within (pp. xxxi)
FOREWORD

AT THE BEGINNING, we anticipate this subject, as presented, will be taken at face value and understood by some, even to many of our profession. Many, in our opinion, possess many preconceived ideas which need reconstruction. We record our knowledge, gained through research, of the underlying fundamentals upon which Chiropractic rests as promulgated by our father but never clearly explained by him. By careful reading of his writings, gleanings of these ideas are apparent.

To be consistent with the objective of this talk, it is written with *we* and us in mind. Ordinarily, "we" and "us" imply and are understood to be *two* distinctly different and separate persons. Ordinarily, "I" implies *one* fellow who lives in a material body and runs it. Whenever and wherever "I" is used, we refer to the educated fellow who thinks, speaks and writes for himself alone as one of the two fellows he is. He does so within the limitations of his education. This book, so far as the author is concerned, writes from the duality of personalities—the inseparable, indivisible, Siamese-twin personalities living in the one structure— the Innate and Educated individualities.

It will be difficult for the reader, as he reads "we," to think "we," because he will constantly interpret it into the ordinary channels of thought of *two* different and separate people. To read this book and gain the viewpoint of its author, the reader must know the "we" or *he* will fail to gain the fundamental purpose of this book.

B. J. PALMER.

---

v. 23 Up From Below the Bottom (pp. vii)

FOREWORD

WE serves several purposes:
1. It eliminates that disgusting and egotistical selfish pronoun "I" which constantly intrudes itself.
2. It permits the author to delineate his concept of the duality of personalities inhabiting one human home.
3. It broadly includes and spreads credit where credit is due, to any, every, and all people who have or are cooperating in building the structures, organizations, institutions, and associations which are an integral part of their lives.

B. J. PALMER.

---

v. 29 1953 Upside Down and Inside Out with B.J. (pp. vii)

ADVANCE EXPLANATION
Going over these stories, in the early part of 1953, in our winter home at Sarasota, Fla...
In this book, at this date, we revised our original writings to make them conform to other recent books from Vol. 21 to 28 by changing "I" to "we," "ours," etc. for same reasons we stated in previous books...

The passage below is B.J.'s description of his enlightenment. According to the quotes above, we know that this transformation from "I" to "We" occurred before 1949. His last writings with "I" were from 1938. This passage is so profound, that only the entire chapter from The Glory Of Going On (1961) will adequately express the experience.

---

v. 37 1961 The Glory of Going On (pp.149-155)
(unabridged)

Chapter Eighteen
THE DEAD STILL LIVE
(The term "I" is used in this story until a later page where B.J. explains why he changes it to "we.")

It is not generally known I possess MANY degrees from MANY universities thruout the world. What kind of universities are these? Where are they located? They are all universities of Hard Knocks. Surprisingly all are located in ONE city, in ONE building, in ONE room, in Davenport, at The P.S.C., in its Osteological Laboratory.

I gazed, bewildered, at the many ramifications OF THOSE universities; looked about stupified, not knowing what to think, where to begin, what to do. It is not generally known I also hold degrees of caveologist, volcanologist, materialist, spiritualist, archeologist, humanitarian, historian, osteologist, and anthropologist.

In this ONE room is the GREATEST university in the world, where time is and is not, was and was not surrounded by the essence of vast numbers of human realities. Many a year, countless hours, I burned midnight oil, up at 3:00 or 4:00 a.m. regularly, that I might pass countless rigid examinations, answering and solving endless human problems.

I approached the multiple doors of this ONE room with hesitation and fear. Dared I open locked doors and boldly walk in? Had I a right to disturb those long-lost sleeps of thousands of tragic souls who were hastened to untimely graves? Had I courage sufficient to dig into their graves, open their coffins, and ask them to tell ME how they died?

In THIS ONE ROOM is contained the largest and finest collection in the world of comparative, anomalous, pathological, and traumatic osteological specimens, more especially of the spinal column. Why this elaboration and preponderance of spinal columns? Because therein IS THE KEY that opens and/or closes ALL doors to ALL knowledge of ALL living unrivaled human activities.

My books, later written, printed, and distributed for depicting what these universities ably demonstrated to ME, are ALL based fundamentally on UNLIMITED evidence, seen, observed, and studied in thousands of these osteological specimens in The B. J. P. Clinic Osteological Laboratory. I have spent thousands of hours studying the records of WHAT INNATE DID under anomalous, pathological, and traumatic living conditions, temporary in any one age and in the eons of evolutionary stages of uninterrupted and deliberate developments. THERE IS WHERE I found PRACTICAL studies which proved limitations of what Innate CAN and CANNOT DO with abnormal anomalous, pathological, or traumatic forms of matter.

In that osteological collection of over 25,000 specimens is an encyclopedia—anything and everything affecting human beings—which any or many could possibly want or need to know. Therein is evidence and proof of the sage of the ages, away up and beyond education, eclipsing that of any or all colleges or universities made of bricks and stones.

In this ONE room, once I had fearlessly entered its portals, I shut out the misguided educational world; and at the same time I opened new avenues where I was surrounded, by a world of thousands of testimonials of the most intelligent personalities the world could exhibit. It was here I dreamed about and had abundance of proof of an incompetent, inefficient world of sick people, to find if possible an escape to conquer, to rehabilitate, to rejuvenate and rebuild, that those who live might be better, brighter, and happier.

As a student of those who came and went, I learned to become a student of those who were here by proxy, and those who were to come, in the pulsating flesh and bone. The evaluations of the past taught ME the necessities of the present and a future.

I entered alone—a stranger in a strange room—surrounded by strange peoples. I little realized as I studied that I would be surrounded with many thousands of kindred friends. I casually met ONE personality after another, all in each, in common alike, who introduced themselves as Mr. and Mrs. Innate. We shook hands; they told ME their life's stories. WE discussed ideas and methods, back and forth, became acquainted, then friendly. Finally, after months and years, we became very close and intimate, a communion of kindred intents and purposes, never varying one thot, one second of time; never broken since, down thru all these years.

Each in his or her turn, finding me interested, introduced me to many another Innate. Eventually, I was in a vast assembly, all eager to tell ME their life's stories. I staggered and stumbled into this ONE room. I entered as a bum, a wandering and roaming hobo, alone, seeking I knew not what. I went IN THAT ONE ROOM with MY mind cluttered, in conflict with the past. It was like a handful of peas rattling and echoing weird sounds in a boiler.

I was like unto an ignorant youth, going into and exploring unknown and unexplored caves, digging for dead skeletons, into the earth, spoonful by spoonful, seeking long-buried artifacts that once lived, whom I hoped would reveal, when pieced together, long-denied and unknown factualities of long-buried truths of people who had been long lied about, shunned, and denied. Many an hour have I seen, looked, meditated, and listened to each tale told by each bone. What were they bringing to light? Who knew?

The misfortunes of each were different—no two alike—as they must have performed their daily chores. The MATTER changed from one family to another, one century to another, but the spirit, ego, soul, personality of the Innate that once lived in each of those homes all spoke ONE universal language, regardless of differences of race, color, nationality, geography, or of the century.

Who was I—a mere stripling of an awkward kid with no education, per se—to think that I could face this cold, cruel world with A NEW idea, a DIFFERENT premise, a PRACTICAL and factual principle and practice which worked, all based on the endless tales these bones spoke?

Who was I, this lean and lanky David with his new minor sling-shot, to think HE alone could pit HIS thots against a merciless, gigantic, greedy series of many major, important, well-established university Goliaths, and overthrow those dynasties of human wrecks strewn everywhere on the paths of health failures? For ME to convince MYself became MY ONE Big Job (B.J.).

These silent reminders of long past existences proved INNATE was an—
architect plumber, draughtsman, welder, engineer, fireman, builder, pump-maker, obstetrician beautician, archeologist, artist carpenter, erector of power stations brick-layer, bridge-builder layer of underground wire systems in all its city streets,
alleys, and homes, electrician camera equipped with automatic adjustable lens endless tape recorder, musical composer, ranging from grand opera to boogie—woogie, color motion picture, thermostat, regulating heating and cooling air conditioner mechanic, sculptor and then producing and reproducing like patterns and products many times—a one-unit, self-contained unit being.

94

Even the mummified Egyptian body of Princess Meritaton, wrapped in hundreds of yards of linen tape, lying peacefully in her coffin with her over—500 artifacts close-by, which were buried with her, 3,500 years ago; her spinograph with its axis subluxation tells a tale of a repetition of how she MIGHT HAVE died in common with many others before and since, because of it. She still speaks a common language I understand in common with all that which surrounds her. Age does not diminish human truth.

These osseous historians left an indelible record written into the libraries of materials made, that all who look and see may again be aware of how great was Innate then or now that made them. These communing personalities of coming-to-life living people were and are an open book, reciting woes, worries, and how they struggled in conflicts within themselves to exist, handicapped with multitudes of insurmountable odds.

IT WAS HERE IN THIS ONE ROOM that Innate taught ME its ways, means, and methods of how it alone produces and reproduces living human bodies; elucidating how normal became abnormal, and how abnormal could once again be rebuilt back to normal—something no university of brick or stone knew or taught.

IN THAT ONE ROOM, I listened to, saw, and understood the brilliance of Innate Intelligence as it toiled, struggled, day after day, week after week, year after year, reshaping, mending, stitching together broken parts, replacing dead tissues with live ones, working consistently side by side with sicknesses and healths, as it toiled to keep those homes intact against the ravages of violence, disasters, wars, storms; and then, when it left that living home, it left behind an indelible record of how "wonderfully and fearfully" it performed its silent miracles to us uneducated people.

WITHIN THIS ONE ROOM there existed thousands of records of WHAT Innate thot; HOW it worked; WHERE it delivered; WHY it did it; successively reconstructing body after body within human and maimed bodies. These deaf, dumb, and blind inarticulate bones spoke vivid living experiences of the struggles to

95

live; how dis-ease bored in and how Innate recon-structed and rebuilt them to keep mind and matter working together pleasantly.

IT WAS IN THAT ONE ROOM where I saw battles raged back and forth between the OUTSIDE-IN, BELOW-UPWARD artificialities which were given to the sick in vain attempts to get them well, in conflict with Innate's way of sending down its forces from ABOVE-DOWN, INSIDE-OUT.

IT WAS HERE IN THIS ONE ROOM where I became unalterably convinced, with a deep conviction which no amount of incongruous and delusive experiments can erase, modify, amend, substitute, or change the logic, reason, evidence, and proof here proven endless times.

IT WAS HERE IN THIS ONE ROOM, the Great Teacher and Master of ALL people of ALL times, was Innate. IT WAS HERE with these retired personalities, with their every-day personal products, I learned the basic truths of Chiropractic and how to become a Chiropractor.

Up till THIS period of MY life, I was INVOLVING MY thots, words, and acts much like so many have done and were doing. The "I" was egotistic as well as egoistic. After THIS period of OUR life, WE began EVOLVING like few people do or have done. From then on, WE thot, spoke, and acted. From then on, "I" was humble in the presence of Innate within as WE lived together.

IT WAS THERE, plus time, IN THIS ONE ROOM, I found MYself. WE found OURselves—INNATE AND I—until EACH lost his or her singular and single identity and became a plural duality, to eventually walk down the byways and highways together the rest of OUR lives.

———————

It was then and there, IN THAT ONE ROOM, WE decided to champion the cause of a sane, sound, sensible philosophy, science, and art, based on the pleas of these thousands of deplorable wrecks of human beings who had dinned their unfortunate sufferings into our minds year after year.

96

Fortified WITH INNATE, WE could march forward forcibly proclaiming a single truth which all the world would some day listen to, heed, and apply. Encouraged, backed and supported by Innate, the Big Job (B.J.) became simple—it was OUR duty which we could not shun, forsake, or cast aside lightly when pressure from without became heavy and the burden hard to bear. Since the days WE came out of that ONE ROOM, WE never have shirked our dual responsibility.

Dare WE challenge the errors and mistakes of past and present? Had WE courage to dispute brains at work in these universities of books and laboratories ? Dare WE call them basic-ally unsound? Wasn't proof of this cemetery sufficient to convince US? What did this weed-grown assemblage of lost souls cry out for INNATE AND ME to do? Could these pleas from graves be denied? Could the tongues of sufferings of those myriads be ignored? Could these wrecks on the pathways of life be denied and forgotten?

WE came OUT OF THAT ONE ROOM, bearing a fiercely burning torch to build a better road on which sick people could travel in their rights to get well and live longer, to prevent and overcome the ravages, horrors, miseries, and pleas of thousands we had seen, talked with, and had become intimately associated with before being placed on exhibition in this ONE room. WE came OUT OF THAT ONE ROOM with the ultimate buying and selling objectives of developing into a science and art; this philosophy of understanding and knowledge, which they told us in so many ways, so frequently; preaching the gospel to many disciples, to spread glad tidings to all peoples everywhere. OUR thots NOW were organized, systematized; our convictions deep and well anchored. All was regulated and channeled into and under perfect control.

WE came OUT OF THAT ONE ROOM a disciple of a just rightcous, and honest cause, to face the world with a clear conscience. It was now OUR responsibility to protect and defend it against traducers who would tend to retard, hinder, and cause this great truth to be lost, and forced back into the womb of the dark ages of ignorant oblivion.

"Dead bones" you say! They ARE dead to most people. TO US they are reminders of people who lived, chatted, spoke, telling countless years of active participation in world affairs. They EDUCATIONALLY spoke many tongues, but they functionally ALL performed ONE UNIVERSAL LANGUAGE. Each osseous specimen is a college degree, a book, a library, a living story of struggles galore of Innate, to retain life in the home it lived in. WE fondled, caressed, loved each individual bone, as a mother fondles, caresses, and loves each child. They WERE now living people to our observant eyes and open mind, ferreting and solving their secrets. Those once lived that WE might live and learn how to save millions from dying before their time; that mind and matter, Innate and function might live together happily and harmoniously.

From one point of view, WE now are a confirmed spiritualist, inasmuch as we have communed with thousands of ghosts IN THIS ONE ROOM where each has haunted us these many years. One by one, differing ghosts of differing nationalities awakened within us a desire to reach into their past lives, to tell us HOW they suffered, struggled, fought to overcome the ravages of dis-ease, accidents, misfortunes, violence. Many of these long-buried bodies became resurrected Innate spirits, became alive once more, which told US tales of endless sufferings, tortures, even to hangings, that WE might learn the great lesson of being a servant to obviate such in years to come; that WE might better serve the world.

People come today. They pass thru this human one room university and gaze upon this bone cemetery. What DO they see? DEAD bones! Today, this conglomerate assemblage of mixed races is but a museum for the curious. They pass thru quickly, understanding no more when they leave than when they entered. To US, INNATE AND I, it was a vast responsibility of a vast presentation of the past, present, and future of millions of human beings, gone and to come.

SOME PSC students and Lyceum visitors never visit this University of Knowledge. SOME come, tarry an hour, wondering

98

why any SANE man would spend a fortune collecting 25,000 dead bones.

They DON'T know! WE DO!

  This ends Book One of *The Spiritual Writings of B.J. Palmer.* As you can see, the period between 1949 and 1952 was voluminous for Palmer. Book Two will focus on his writings from 1955 to 1961. As before, there will be some crossover, but the tone of the topics will be set by the focus of the writings from this second period. Most of the writings that follow were written after Palmer turned seventy-five.

B.J.'s 75th

Book Two: The Final Teachings
Volumes 32-39; (1955-1961)

DEDICATION (from volume 37, 1961 pp. 7)

To those myriads of pioneers and their successors who ably followed in their footsteps down thru these years, helping to defend, protect, and preserve this philosophy, science, and art of a specific, pure, unadulterated, two-hands Chiropractic; to those loyal undeviating thousands who stood close-by, ardently espousing and generously developing an inner depth of consciousness into the inner Innate, attaining the enlightenment; to every disciple and patient who has stood hard-by during those lean years in the propagation of our helpful service to a sick world, we give our bounteous thanks which they so richly deserve.

Book Two explores the development of many of the theories from Book One. The main difference in the organization of the chapters is that they are more loosely bound by topics. While this period of Palmer's writing was filled with many new insights, the main concepts can be clustered into larger groupings. For this reason, chapters in this book will contain sub-headings. These are placed in boldfaced type above the quote's reference. This will help the reader to distinguish different ideas within each topic.

In these later years, Palmer was struggling with illness. His political and business duties were mostly done. He spent much time in Sarasota, Florida and completed eight more texts, three of which were published posthumously by his son David, the new President of The Palmer School of Chiropractic.

In these final teachings, B.J. explains for us the essence of genius. He relates it to the contact with innate, but goes deeper and views it as a fount of unlimited energy and wisdom. It is from here that all of the great geniuses and prophets and saints drew from. He also goes into greater detail as to the historical origination of humanity's fragmentation into two distinct intelligences; educated and innate. He explains a theory about the evolution of consciousness. In this regard, he mentions Eden, Evolution, Involution, and the salvation of humanity; which would be a restoration of the flow of the innate.

Finally, he focuses his view of man's divinity. Although this was apparent in the previous period of his writings, here he says that the chiropractor adjusts, and allows the "living God, in living Man," to be liberated. Thus the chiropractor becomes "an Apostle to the living God." Clearly, as we saw in the dedication above, that he is talking about an enlightenment that is both spiritual and transformational.

Chapter 13
On Tapping into the inner potential

In this chapter, we have more of B.J.'s discussion of the self-actualizing individual. This is the person who can access the unlimited fountain within. He also discusses in this chapter an even deeper issue, that of enlightenment. I have included excerpts from a chapter where Palmer analyzes a book that was then just published; *The Circle of Faith*, by Marcus Bach, which examined the enlightenment of certain individuals. B.J. admonishes the author to focus his writings on helping the reader to go within, and even goes so far as to tell Bach that he should have instructed the spiritual teachers that he interviewed to go within instead of seeking enlightenment from others on the outside. Also in this chapter are sections on the use of positive language and the importance of disciplining the mind.

Here we find B.J. discussing the third aspect to the innate transformation; opening to the infinite. As noted in the beginning of Book One, the first two levels of awakening for B.J. were to acknowledge the majesty of innate, and then be guided by that wisdom. Now we have clear explanations about what happens when man humbles and sublimates his ego to the great wisdom pervading not only his tissue cells, but the inner workings of the cosmos, the infinite; he becomes it.

B.J. at the foot of giant Buddha, Ayuthia, Thailand, 1924

On Controlling the Mind

v. 36 1958 Law of Life (pp. 18)

SOW WITH HARVEST IN MIND

We can't beat the law of cause and effect. What goes into the past has got to come out of the future. What we sow we must eventually reap. But we can start today to plant seeds of a better life for ourselves. We can never hope to know all laws, nor can we understand all mysteries which govern both body and mind.

But we can understand enough to be, to a very great extent, "masters of our fate." I am convinced by replacing negative, destructive and unwholesome thoughts with constructive, courageous and helpful thoughts, we can improve our health, relationships with others and chances for success and happiness. Control of mind is very often control of causes. Let us open our minds and discipline our thoughts and actions, that we may better understand God's laws and become more efficient workers and "masters of our fate."

On Positive Thinking

v. 27 1951 History Repeats (pp. 736)

PARADOX OF COMMANDMENTS.
The Ten Commandments are presumed to encompass the Golden Rule; they are so broad and long that the latitude and longitude cover every human endeavor. Yet, they have failed. They are ten in number, nine are negative and only one remains positive. "Thou Shalt NOT—" do this or that. Tell a boy he must NOT and he WILL. Tell humanity they shall NOT and they will violate an oath to do it. Commandments were written to prevent doing the thing they fasten upon you. The paradox! Who ever wrote the Commandments did not know psychology or he would have written them in positive and then they would have accomplished, at least, more than they do.

"KEEP SMILING" suggests a smile; it suggests KEEP smiling. Some wag, thinking to improve upon our phraseology, invented "DON'T WORRY." The negativeness of the "DON'T" makes you want to do it. "It" is WORRY, the word suggests the thing they wanted to take you from.

---

v. 23 1950 Up From Below (pp. 464-5)

I went into a department store in Milwaukee a short time ago to buy some suspenders, socks and handkerchiefs. Some suspenders hung on a rack over the showcase. I was looking at them. Three clerks were selling each other their impressions of a dance of the night before. They were also trying to sell each other a chewing gum racing-match. Butting into the "sale" I asked if one of them cared to show me suspenders.

Said she, "Is there anything YOU want?"
"No," said I, "I am here to roll a peanut up the hill." She giggled. The suspenders I was looking at were 98 cents. She gave me the once over.

Said she, "I have some cheaper ones down here." I wonder if she correctly sized me up. She finally sold me a pair for 49 cents. "Is there anything else you want?" I mentioned hose. She trailed me to another counter, another girl and said, "This man wants to buy something." I had mentioned hose. There were some silk hose laying on the counter, box open; I looked at them. They were marked $1.25. Without paying any attention to me the girl dived down and brought up some marked 59 cents, which I bought.

She then said, "There's NOTHING ELSE you want, is there?" to which I replied, "No, you have just said there is 'nothing else' I want." Is that girl "selling herself?" She is selling eight hours of time, not even eight hours of service, much less goods. That girl wonders why she doesn't advance in position, salary, etc.

On Enlightenment

v. 34 1957 Evolution or Revolution (pp. 18)

The finite education of man has long sought to uncover, discover, fathom the secret innermost recesses of the infinite which surrounds him, which governs, directs, rules, and pre-determines the universal and everlasting rules and regulations of living things, including himself.

Like all living objects, man is born, exists a while, dies, and disintegrates, to be born again and again in another form of matter. Each unit is educationally a NEW beginning, yet it IS an OLD continuation of the source that produced HIM.

Man is born with NO education. He assembles external impressions from the OUTSIDE world beyond himself, interprets them, and soon realizes there is a world OUTSIDE himself greater than his limited education knows. He seeks to know the greater OUTSIDE world. Yet INSIDE HIM is that greater INSIDE world he does not know, seldom recognizes, never fully understands. His limited finite understanding seeks to know the infinite unlimited world surrounding him, but fails dismally to realize that world he seeks is WITHIN HIM. Should that time come when his finite mind could and did KNOW the infinite mind WITHIN, then his external finite mind would cease to be, because it would then be infinite in scope, understanding, and application. His "education," per se, would cease to be, because it would be humble by comparison. It is well for the human race that the infinite has been placed beyond the reach of the finite, for WITH IT we have cosmos; WITHOUT IT would be chaos.

Fortunately, the infinite has seen fit to bury itself so far beyond the reach of the finite that it never can be or will be reached. All education CAN DO, or has a proprietary right to do, is to see its work and works, acknowledge that such is, admit its endless potentials, accept it as is, permit it to produce and reproduce what it will, as it will, placing no artificial interferences in its natural path; and, if such DO exist, to correct them to permit the infinite to work its will thru the finite man and matter as best it can, unmolested. THIS, man has yet to learn—that WITHIN HIM is an infinite at work, greater than he knows.

B.J. at foot of Buddha of Ayuthia, Thailand 1925

v. 34 1957 Evolution or Revolution (pp. 68)

These original and uninhibited thinkers and seekers of NEW truths were unshackled—not constrained or constricted, not bound within the limitations of OLD principles.

When such a mind was at liberty he could recognize A NEW WORKABLE AND WORKING PRINCIPLE ENCOMPASSED **WITHIN** MAN.

Human beings, of all countries and times, have a common denominator. They revere, idolize, idealize, and place high on pedestals of fame such persons as Mohammet, Buddha, Confucious, Christ, Mary Baker Eddy—not because they WERE "ignorant" but because they knew HOW to draw down from within those permanent PRINCIPLES which were practical when taught and practiced, from which all profited.

Human beings are divisible into two groups:
(a) those who have "found themselves" from above down, inside out
(b) those who are lost in the confusion of the wilderness, who seek a way out from OUTSIDE IN, BELOW UPWARD.

The "a" group become leaders. The "b" group TRY to follow by arrogantly forcing their OUTSIDE-IN, BELOW-UPWARD INvolution theories into the practical ABOVE-DOWN, INSIDE-OUT EVolution PRINCIPLES. This is why there are so few of the "a" group and so many of the "b" group...

On Genius

v. 36 1958 Law of Life (pp. 49)

(If I could have worked at the bench along side Edison, and helped him bring forth the electric globe, batteries, talking machine, motors, and millions of applications to which he put Franklin's key sparks, what a thrill that would have been knowing we were a participant in revolutionizing the labors of a forthcoming new era for mankind.)

You HAVE this opportunity. YOU have it NOW!

YOU, who now listen to OUR VOICE have such an oppor-tunity pregnant with even GREATER potentials than what Newton, Franklin, Darwin, Morse, Bell, Einstein, Edison or Wright Brothers produced because YOU are tapping **the source** of **every**thing **every** man **has ever** produced, therefore are producing a BETTER, HEALTHIER, MORE NORMAL and NATURAL, MENTAL and PHYSICAL MAN, WHO CAN THEN PRODUCE BETTER THINGS THAN THOSE MEN PRODUCED.

Till the advent of PROVABLE LAWS, all concepts of a God were rudimentary and doctrinal, which bewildered pathetic under-standings of THE FORCES OF THE UNIVERSE.

As man studied THE CREATED and began to understand THE LAWS of created objects, he better knew THE LAWS OF THE CREATOR and was able to coordinate himself in relation TO AND WITH AND HOW THE CREATOR PERFORMED HIS WORKS.

The dropping of an apple, hitting Newton's head was a **simple** incident. Undoubtedly similar incidents happened to other people many times. As **simple** as this incident, Newton asked: **"Why** did the apple FALL? WHY didn't it GO UP instead?"** This started a series of NEW and ORIGINAL thinking which developed into NEWTON'S LAW OF GRAVITATION which was the explanation for the LAW OF PHYSICS which had not been so seen or known previously...

On Super Conscious Intelligence

v. 37 1961 Glory of Going On (pp. 58-59)

If educated man would think LESS of too much scholastic educational training, and DEPEND MORE upon Innate thot-flashes, he could and would take his place amongst the original thinkers of history who conceive greater understandings of dormant potentials WITHIN HIM, which are usually submerged by contrast.

(In the egotistic exaggeration of his ego, man speaks of "the other fellow," his "conscience," "that something" in behind, as a "SUB-conscious, NON-conscious, UN-conscious" mind; as tho HE, with his "conscious" mind was the greater. Any intellect great enuf to build a completed child-unit in 280 days, when man with his boastful "education" could not make ONE tissue cell and cause it to functionate life, is NOT BENEATH OR INFERIOR to his petty thinking. In reality, reality, IT is a SUPER-conscious intellect.)

Commenting on Marcus Bach's book, *The Circle of Faith*:

v. 34 1957 Evolution or Revolution (pp. 88-91)

Those people and principles which ARE NOW considered by many to be unusual, freakish, erratic, will be commonplace tomorrow. What IS NOW considered genius, inspiration, "revelations from God," will be a constant in service to all men who will be at peace within themselves and not in conflict with the outside world, which is squeezing them into perversions by artificial means, methods, materials, with obnoxious destructions to themselves.

109

THE FUTURE man will not be a factory-manufactured, bottle-fed, spoon-fluid, hypodermic-injected substitute from OUTSIDE-IN, BELOW-UPWARD sick creature. He will rely entirely on the natural, simple flow of his life-health source from ABOVE-DOWN, INSIDE-OUT.

The future? As a result of the REVOlution now in progress, EVOlution will follow. Many now are realizing the potentials of Innate within. They will help make it possible for additional mankind to keep open the channels of communication between abstract and concrete, that function may be free to flow, that he may become an intellectual giant and be of honest and sincere service to his fellowman, regardless of country, creed, class, color, or religion.

MAN HAS NOT IMPROVED HIMSELF WITHIN HIM-SELF. With this NEW Chiropractic principle of the bigness of the fellow within, the FUTURE man will permit IT to govern his every cell, action, function, all flowing from ABOVE-DOWN, INSIDE-OUT. As a result, MAN HIMSELF, WITHIN HIMSELF, WILL BECOME A BETTER MAN—more natural and normal, more peaceful, satisfied, contented. AS MORE MEN BECOME BETTER MEN WITHIN THEMSELVES, MORE AND BETTER PRINCIPLES WILL SPRING FORTH FROM THE SOURCE IN MORE MEN, and some day the world will become a decent place for healthy and sane people to live. This IS prophetic because it is an existing fact of what is known BY A FEW OF the present generation, which in the future will be known and practiced BY ALL.

There IS an inevitable future. What use man may make of the difference between ABOVE-DOWN, INSIDE-OUT; and OUTSIDE-IN, BELOW-UPWARD; and HOW TO PRESERVE, PROTECT, PERPETUATE, and defend that difference, depends upon the vision of our people and how far and how soon they overcome medical hurdles which, like wrecks, are strewn all along the road man wishes to travel. As radical and impossible as these postulate processes sound, it works internally in spite of us; and works efficiently if WE work WITH IT…

...of great value, live them, permit them to act thru the OUTER fellow, raising him UP to loftier heights by contrast to the small OUTER fellow who limits his observations to his EXTERNAL self and others like himself, for he sees in others only what he sees in himself—the limitations of education of the OUTER world as viewed by the limited scope of his horizons of his OUTER senses.

As ORDINARY people lived, and as they saw and studied thots, deeds, and accomplishments of EXTRAORDINARY men, they realized that these EXTRAORDINARY men had found buried WITHIN themselves acres of intellectual diamonds to which they learned to listen, which gave them a greater perspective of themselves, which drove them to a greater value in services to their fellow beings. As they studied OTHERS who seemingly were "geniuses", or had "inspirations" or "revelations from God," they began to realize that BURIED WITHIN THEMSELVES were THE SAME great potentials. By either deliberate or latent talents, they opened the gates frozen to most men betwixt and BETWEEN the INNER and OUTER fellows IN themselves, the same as other people have done about whom you write. They realized THEY POSSESSED the same greater potentials IF they would permit THEM to come thru by minimizing the OUTER small fellow, letting the MAXIMUM INNER fellow take precedence in their thots and actions.

You produce examples of people who HAVE FOUND THEMSELVES. You write about what THEY have done, but you do not speak in simple terms which would teach other men HOW to look INSIDE AND UPWARD to the greater fellow INSIDE THEM, except to enlarge upon how to use their education to look OUTSIDE other men. If you looked INSIDE each person, you could show him A GREATER PATH to follow. Your book does not lay down the principle that WITHIN MAN, WITHIN REACH of the OUTER man, is an INNER VOICE that is far more powerful IF he would let it flow thru. I know you do cite innumerable instances where the OUTER man of ONE person seeks the OUTER thots and activities of OTHER men. Some isolated individuals recognize the power INSIDE and let it come thru by subjugating the insignificant OUTER fellow—what you call sublimation of self.

You describe other persons who HAVE found themselves, but you do not TELL HIM that WITHIN him are THE SAME great potentials usually undiscovered, unfound, untold in the mass. The ONLY WAY to find himself is by sublimating the OUTER fellow and maximizing the tremendous potentials hidden in his INNER self. Even Schweitzer possessed this development, SPIRITUALLY, but when it came to his being a physician and healing and curing his sick, he did not possess this insight materially, for it was then HE REVERSED THE PHYSICAL PROCESS and was treating MATTER from OUTSIDE-IN…

"Genius" is not secret of a few. It is buried in all. You write about those who have dug deep, dug up, and put on exhibition what "genius" is. But what is more important is to arouse that same genius that is up-high buried in ALL people. If this were not so, they would be dead and buried, for THEY do represent THE genius that built them, runs them every day they live. To recognize IT, let IT shine thru the dense dark deep jungles of too much superficial education, should be the work of those who HAVE FOUND THEMSELVES, as you are doing.

The same Innate that inhabits the body of the Educated fellow named Marcus Bach is the same Innate that inhabits the body of the Educated fellow named B. J. Palmer. How do we know? Because THE BODY that the Innate made in the fellow called Marcus Bach is the same kind of body that the Innate made in the fellow called B. J. Palmer. The patterns are like two peas in a pod. This rule holds good IN ALL species and families, each product true to its producer, with no difference in pattern from which each is molded. The pattern, mold, product of the Innate Builder is Universal Added and compiled, ALL Innates equal the Universal Intelligence.

The Innate pattern flowing from ABOVE-DOWN, INSIDE-OUT, from which the international human family is cast, is inflexible. It becomes abortive only when the Educated OUT-SIDE- IN, BELOW-UPWARD tries to modify, amend, and change THAT PATTERN millions of times, countless ways; but in spite of it all, THE PATTERN remains fixed.

This being a truism—that the Innate pattern of ALL people IS fixed, stable, internally-eternal, and is alike in all—then each educated person has the same right to turn on the internal faucet BETWEEN Innate IN him and permit it to flow into his Educated, the same as the Christ, Buddha, Therese, Shogni, Helen, Pope Pius, Albert, or any other individual had, about whom you write in your book. But, by contrast, what HAS happened? The Educated of peoples looks to the manifestations of the Innate in the Christ for aid, comfort, assistance, help, life everlasting, thinking THAT is the ONE and only source of salvation to arrive at the destination HE—the Educated fellow— wants to attain. All any man has to do is to GO UPSTAIRS IN HIS GARRET to find everything he spiritually wants and needs. It is not consistent that he vacate HIS Educated basement, go outside HIS Innate garret, and go burrowing or borrowing into the Innate garret of Christ, Buddha, Therese, Shogni, Helen, Pope Pius, Albert, or any other individual to find what he seeks internally.

This question of dependency of one person leaning upon another for mental, moral, or spiritual integrity support, is based on the theory that by ourself we can do little, if anything; but leaning on the crutches of others gives us education, morals, and confidence in self. If this attitude were sound, we could carry it further: If one father and mother wanted a child they should call for physical action from another father and mother; or if one family wanted health instead of sickness, they should seek it from other people, never from within themselves; or, in the terms of medicine, we should rely upon drugs, injections, antibiotics from OUTSIDE-IN, BELOW-UPWARD. We need go no further than WITHIN the confines of oneself to secure confidence, morals, health, life. In cases of religions, however, we step backward into antiquity, 2000 years, and seek everything we think we want and need, ask for it, pray for it, in the name of a Deity, and it will come running merely because we recite what we want, and it will fall into our laps with little or no action upon our part.

As well think educationally that we should have faith and belief in aid from another to help us digest food, urinate or defecate, for functional activity in our body matter, as to think educationally we

113

must look to and depend upon antiquity for guidance spiritually, for aid and comfort which we can and should give ourselves from WITHIN ourselves, and then condemn others OUTSIDE our self if we don't get it.

True, so long as man and woman are an integral part of society that must depend upon each other for EXTERNAL relationships, just as man depends upon woman and woman upon man for the propagation of the race, or they rely upon others for commercial services, etc.; but when it comes TO THE INDI-VIDUAL and ALL HIS INTERNAL MENTAL AND PHYSICAL PROCESSES, here he must rely upon his INTERNAL MENTAL AND PHYSICAL RESOURCES alone.

Here is what is considered to be the proper religious thing to do. The OUTSIDE-IN, BELOW-UPWARD educated Mr. A observes and sees the supremely efficient manifestation performed by the ABOVE-DOWN, INSIDE-OUT Innate in Christ. INSIDE... I am not designedly trying to belittle the divinity of the Christ, but I AM saying that the Divinity of Infinity is IN ALL of us, the same as it was in Him.

Somehow, as we read your THE CIRCLE OF FAITH, you seemingly missed ONE dominant contrast that IT IS A STRAIGHT LINE from OUTSIDE-IN, BELOW-UPWARD between these two approaches, calling the INNER man God, Therese, Shogni, Helen, Pope Pius. Albert, Christ, or whatever other name you will—THEY caught the greater understanding that WITHIN THEM was something greater than what the ordinary run-of-the-mill men had been educated NOT TO find.

At times and in places there was a sentence or two where you almost had this understanding that other men and women had who found their greatness inside themselves, the same as many others in history, and it was this common likeness that they found themselves which made them see it in others. Some of these sentences showed you WERE TRYING to say what we think and hope we have said here. Would that you had said more of it in each personality you visited, saw, talked with, who HAD found that

114

which you were seeking to find FROM them, which they found IN THEMSELVES.

This seemingly new-old outlook to many, and old-new out-look to the few, may seem most radical; but if it is natural, normal, common-sense, simple, and single, the "awareness" path all men have trodden who moved worlds, then it is "radical" ONLY to those conservatives who prefer to sit idly by and twiddle their thumbs, who have no desire or interest in wanting to improve the status quo of the suffering masses who so badly need being shaken loose.

Later: The above study of THE CIRCLE OF FAITH was sent to Marcus Bach. After studying same, he replies:

"This is the first chance I have had to thank you for your penetrating critique on CIRCLE OF FAITH.

"I darn well appreciated your common sense approach. Reason is that which makes all things reasonable, and I am happy that in the midst of all sorts of comments on this new book, you related it to the ABOVE-DOWN INSIDE-OUT concept. That this is the secret of the 'great ones' and that it is the same potential expressed within different physical beings, is what Leibnitz called the 'Perennial Philosophy,' the vertical-ABOVE- DOWN, horizontal-INSIDE-OUT figure.

"Health, blessings and creative power to you always!

"Fondly, Marc."

115

Chapter 14
On The Evolution of Consciousness

In this chapter, Palmer discusses the different levels of consciousness that developed in human history due to the onset of reason. He mentions a time when humans awakened to Cosmic Awareness and tried to bring others beyond reason to the innate within. The reason was too powerful and the drive toward an innate embrace never happened, thus we are left with the dilemma of today, the great divide. He also discusses a new age that will dawn when this realization is experienced by the masses. The new level of consciousness is the drive within matter of the universal intelligence, or God, to know itself.

On The Fall from Eden & Development into the New Perspective

v. 38 1961 The Great Divide (pp. 3-6)

Chapter I
THE GREAT DIVIDE
HOW TRUE WE STATE THE SOCIAL EDUCATIONAL PROBLEM

THERE IS A NEW dimension to life and a new perspective that the majority of mankind are unaware of, but which the sages and prophets have continually tried to point out. It is said that the letter of the word killeth, but the spirit of the word give it Life. We see the world as it was formed in seven days, and how man evolved from the sea and for the period of time until the faculty of Reasoning came upon him he was living in a state of perfection for that moment of time and space and then came the period of time which people with their educated intellects have interpreted as a particular episode in the Garden of Eden. *It is apparent that the fall of man involved a long period of time where they started going out from under control and putting emphasis on their newly acquired faculties of Reasoning governed by the outer educated mind, which in itself is nothing and miniature compared to the Innate mind which is the positive controlling source of all that is.*

Years passed and man in keeping with the design of life gradually took on more and more new faculties: the awareness of music, awareness of color, the awareness of environment, etc. It seems that first one person would come into awareness of a new faculty, then a few more people would come unto it, then gradually the members of the people with this new faculty would compound upon itself until it was common to the majority of mankind and became accepted in their search for understanding.

We came into a faculty of Cosmic Awareness and as time goes on more and more people came into this awareness and their primary motive for being *was recognition of the distorted path* that man was treading and they tried to bring back right direction, in other words an awareness of this Universal Intelligence and *how simple life can be if only people would look within and let their Innate doeth the works.*

We see the period of time when many Prophets and Philosophers became illuminated to this awareness and tried desperately to portray it to their followers from the Cosmic aspect and some of them came into illumination themselves but those who followed *were educated men without Innate awareness and they followed the letter of the word rather than the spirit.* Voices *from the source,* in their own language, and, it is understandable now that the *voice which has been guiding us over these years is that small wee voice which spoke to them. What is interesting is that this voice speaks without audible sound and comes more as an impression. What is beautiful is that there is no doubting it and it is an absolute positive expression which cannot be denied or refuted.*

If only people would let the barnacles which encrust their hulls start falling away and listen from within long enough to let this tremendous source of power start manifesting itself through them, the so-called problems of life would soon be eliminated. There can be an unfettered simple joy of life which is difficult to put into words.

As the great mass of the unwashed become indoctrinated into this newer and greater understanding in the deeper internal depths of the potentials within, into this newer and greater understanding, then as numbers multiply and its application is practically applied to more and more, the movement will take on growth. Eventually mankind profits and a new era of evolution is established into the lives of our people.

At present there is a deep rooted, artificially produced conflict between the outside-in, below-upward, super educated campaign being thrust into the minds of the greater unthinking mass; and, the normal, natural and healthy Innate flow from above down, inside out. The physical seemingly is in the ascendancy even into our ranks.

The more practical and working chiropractic philosophy, science and art will eventually, given time for our adherents to multiply into its broader understanding, in its application to man-kind, it will take root into a master evolution of a greater vision of service to mankind in all his ways of living.

People have the word Spiritual fouled up like everything else. The design for life to be under right function is to be creative not for one's self, but for the good of others and the whole body of mankind. *Actually anyone that is creative is a Spiritual figure. That would be us, Edison, Ford, Wright Brothers, great architects, artists, and all the luminaries that have benefited man since the beginning of time.*

We can see thru the pages of history those people that have obtained a true Innate Awareness HAVE NOT BEEN HIGHLY EDUCATED MEN, NOT SOCIALLY INCLINED, NOT BE-CAUSE IT WAS DENIED THEM, ONLY THAT THEIR EMPHASIS TO LIVING WAS CRAMMED INTO THAT SMALL OUTER SO-CALLED EDUCATED MIND WHICH WAS BUT A FRACTION OF THE REAL POTENTIAL WHICH WAS INTERNALLY AVAILABLE IF MEN WILL LET IT FLOW FROM ABOVE-DOWN, INSIDE-OUT.

THE PATH WE HAVE HEWED THROUGH OUR LIFE IS VERY OBVIOUS. In the beginning, in our work, there were those who followed us, who could cope with, keep up with and followed our internal levels of thinking. As we progressed the number of people gradually progressed, some dropping by the way side...

There doesn't seem much good to condemn those who disagree with our thots, because they don't' know better and are doing the best they can, for what they think they know. What is beautiful to perceive is that the number of our people coming into this Innate

118

awareness is multiplying upon itself and the numbers are reaching a point that is making the world aware THAT A NEW FACULTY IS COMING TO MANKIND AND IN TIME IT COULD BE THE NEW AGE THAT MAN IS LOOKING FOR.

Our Innate and the love FLOWING THRU US FROM ABOVE-DOWN, INSIDE-OUT reaches out to each of you and in addition our gratitude and thanks are unmeasured for what you have done, not for us, but for what can be done through us in the service of others.

---

v. 22 1949 The Bigness of the Fellow Within (pp. 32)

Conditioned on these premises the history of evolution is the story of how this inward something has struggled to burst the chains and walls of its material limitations, in its striving to attune itself to the vibrations of the universe.

Nor have we reasons for believing the limit of its evolution has been reached. Driven by an insatiable desire, urged by the realization that there are yet myriads of harmonies which are not registered by our present senses, this inward something will evolve new senses, until the human mind and soul reflect, with greater accuracy, the qualities of the all-knowing, ever-present, all-powerful principle we call GOD.

1920's B.J. with staff

119

v. 22 1949 The Bigness of the Fellow Within (pp. 32)

It is true we are spiritual, using the body as an instrument.

It is true Innate Intelligence has constructed the eyes, ears, nose, etc., to register the universal vibrations.

It is true we are finite beings living in an infinite universe.

It is true the five special senses are limited to register but a few of the infinite number of vibrations that do exist.

It is true there are an infinite number of vibrations beyond the range of our sense organs.

It is true our idea of the nature of the universe is pitifully unreal.

On The Great Divide

v. 38 1961 The Great Divide (pp. 11-13)

A GREAT DIVIDE OCCURRED ABOUT 500 B.C., as near as history records. Theles was the Greek philosopher who ob-served two factors in living man which changed all thinking from that day to this. He looked at living man and saw the abstract AND concrete; mind AND matter; inanimate and animate bodies; dead and alive structures. He conceived a necessity that they *be separated*, one from another.

In the hypothetical abstract, they ARE separate. In living realities they CANNOT be separated. For purposes of study of principles and practices, Theles separated one from another; divided the indivisible.

—From that day to this, indivisible has been divisible, from above-down, inside-out.

—Two schools of thought were established from that day to this:

—the physical, material, corporeal were given to students of *physical* properties out of which have come the terms "physic . . . ian" and MATERIA media;

—The spirit, soul, meta-physical were given to the students of spiritual interpretations, out of which have come the psychiatrist, metaphysician, hypnotist, christian scientist.

—Two types of schools were established; physical and spiritual; and two schools of teaching began to meet those concepts.

—And we have had an indivisible divided LIVING sick man mentally and physically, ever since. Each half says it is the whole-mind is all and everything; or body is all and everything.

—One says you can have light with electricity alone—no need for a globe;

—others say you can have light *with* the globe alone—no need for electricity.

—One says if you educationally think right, you'll be right;

—if you educationally think wrong, you'll be wrong.

—One says if you educationally are careful what comes in from outside, both mental OR physical, you'll be mentally or physi-cally healthy;

—if you prevent mental or physical external environment from affecting your insides, you'll internally be mentally and physically normal.

—One is all mental, and no body; other is all body and no mind.

—What is mind? Never matter!

—What is matter? Never mind!

—Both are right as far as they go. Both are wrong because they are only half right; they ignore other half.

—Each is half wrong by itself alone. Both are right WHEN THEY ARE TOGETHER. Mental *and* physical, spiritual *and* corporeal, cannot be separated in LIVING man.

—They are together, always have been together, NEVER WERE separated, cannot NOW be separated—in LIVING man.

—Both of these schools of thought ignored UNITY of both TOGETHER— spiritualists fails because he does not know why or how to UNITE the two; Physician fails to get sick people well because he does not know who to make possible THE UNITY of the two together.

—*Without* Universal Intelligence there would be no moving, functioning, living world;

—*without* Innate Intelligence there would be no moving, functioning, living man;

—matter yes; intelligence yes. Both can be in the hypothetical abstract.

We have no way of knowing there is Universal or Innate Intelligence, except as they speak a Universal or Innate function through LIVING things through which they express themselves. Sooner "educated" man realizes all this and studies LIVING man as a UNITY of mind and matter; spirit and body; Innate and function, the quicker he can and will better serve man in getting him well when sick, making him normal when abnormal, making the insane sane, making the criminal a natural internal law-abiding citizen.

BIG job of the Chiropractor is to preach this new-old gospel to a topsy-turvy unreasonable "educated" world. And, before YOU get misconception is to what we are saying, let us clarify one simple point:

—We do not decry or belittle any and all "education," per se, *when* it is practical and works;

—we do emphatically decry all and any so called medical "education" scientific or other wise, when it is impractical and can't, don't and won't work.

—We decry and belittle all "education" premised on A DISUNITY of mind and matter—and this applies to everything medical, in all its principles and practices, regardless of whether it be mental or physical fields.

v. 38 1961 The Great Divide (pp. 20-1)

The world of today is basically materialistic, grossly sub-stance matter. That which is above and beyond matter has been too largely ignored, forgotten, overlooked. All nature—which is too crude a word to use for such a brilliant performer and performance—*always* strikes its balance. Call it "God" if you prefer, which is an unknown non-personal term for an unknown quantity in religion; or, if you wish a more expressive and more understandable term, We call it UNIVERSAL INTELLIGENCE. Regardless of term, IT ALWAYS strikes a balance, between

a. night and day
b. sun and shadow
c. four seasons of year
d. hot and cold
e. oceans and lands
f. abstracts and matter
g. animal, vegetable and mineral
h. male and female
i. light and darkness
j. births and deaths
k. joys and sorrows
l. mind and matter
m. causes and effects
n. inhalations and exhalations
o. drinking and urination
p. muscles in pairs
q. contractions and relaxations
r. intelligence to equal matter it controls, governs and directs

123

s. in the unit, intelligence to balance function
t. mind to direct matter it controls
u. energy to motivate action in substance
v. spiritual and physical
w. normal and abnormal
Somewhere, somehow, beyond reach of man, this is true with each and every living object, including biped genus homo. Health and life is a balanced use of one, in and through the other.

Sickness is UNbalanced relationships somewhere BETWEEN LIFE on one side of the scale AND DEATH on the other; degree depending upon to what degree scales arc UNBALANCED of one to, into and through the other. Insanity, sickness, pathologies, symbolized an UNBALANCE of function *between* source and expression.

Vertebral subluxations, sequentially followed by occlusions, pressures, interferences, unbalance the alliance, affiliation between norm in Production in brain; REDUCED NORM in transmission in tissue cells.

Aches, pains, sufferings, discomforts, are unbalanced *afferent* impressions based on unbalanced *inferior* impressions as *afferently* transmitted to brain where mind tests incoming reduced quantity of sense perception compared with norm interpretation, difference in the degree of suffering cited.

Sickness, dis-ease, pain and sufferings, are *unbalanced* ex-pressions of abnormal norms on both efferent and afferent sides of the brain, via-efferent-nerve-to-tissue-cell and returning via-tissue-cell-to afferent-nerve-to-brain-cell. A vertebral subluxation is unbalanced relationship between its co-respondents above and below. To give an adjustment is to *restore* balance, channels of communication are opened between mind and matter. Innate being present flows ITS balance from ITS balanced storehouse, into and through ITS balanced material channels, between mind and matter; and, thus, establishes ITS independent, natural and normal balance; something no educated man can do WITHIN HIMSELF, much less doing so in mind and matter *of another* like person who is sick.

All a Chiropractor wants to do, hopes to do, tries to do, or should do, is to open *the* communication with *the* communicant to an established internal balance in the body of another. When mind and matter, mental impulse in matter, and nor mal quantity of nerve force flow through nerves has re-established its norm balance, sick man gets well. What do we mean by "balance" as applied here? It is where MENTAL factor equals PHYSICAL element; where each is 100 per cent from one TO, INTO AND THROUGH the other.

---

v. 39 1961 Our Masterpiece (pp. 33)

The church, psychologist, mentalist, scientifically researches the Bible, God, Soul, Spirit, Ego, Personality, sane and insane. Then the three get their scientific researches, piecing them together—with what result?
Medical men with medical profession, with *materia* medica from *outside-in, below-upward* for 5,000 years, has failed to do what Tic alone has done since 1895.

As a result, they come out with THE GREAT DIVIDE—things spiritual to churches of all denominations, with sectional sects, creeds, and conflicts; and physic-ians of *material* schools, with theoretical inconsistent trials by errors; no permanency; "hit or miss, I give him this." "East is East and West is West, and ne'er the twain shall meet."

---

v. 34 1957 Evolution or Revolution (pp. 10)

What is intelligence, knowledge? There is no such except as THIS factor, passing THRU matter, USING that factor, RECOGNIZES itself. But without matter thru which it manifests itself, there would be no such recognizable by man as such.

---

v. 34 1957 Evolution or Revolution (pp. 32)

The complete pattern of Universal Law is summed up in one word—EVOlution—unfolding FROM WITHIN OUT, from ground to trunk, to branch, to bud, to fruit. Man follows THAT pattern.

B.J. 1925

Chapter 15
On Living God In Living Man

This final chapter sums up all of Palmer's writings on spirituality, religion, healing, and chiropractic. As controversial as it may seem, it is a logical development of his thought as well as his spirituality. If God is in man as the personification of the intelligence pervading all creation, and if the nervous system allows for that expression to occur, then the chiropractic adjustment becomes the means for that expression to materialize, and thus the chiropractor is as a spiritual midwife to the inner essence that is at the heart of all meaning and truth in the universe. If the adjustment is the way for humans to get closer to God, then the chiropractor performs a sacred rite.

---

v. 37 1961 The Glory of Going On (pp. 249-50)

Let us not limit these greater things to come. Let us have THE DISTANT VISION of the eagle, heed our ways WITH FORWARD OUTLOOK, and perhaps let the uniformed majority fall by the wayside; but LET US move forward and upward, unafraid; place OUR TRUST IN THE HIGH POWER ABOVE AND BEYOND AND WITHIN US, in our decisions in getting sick people well and staying well, chiropractically...

Meanwhile, those who violate must be driven out of our temple built by the loving hands of a dedicated and devoted series of pioneers who sacrificed themselves and their all to protect, defend, and save this noble work from being desecrated and destroyed. CHIROPRACTIC WILL SURVIVE, WILL LIVE. NO GREAT TRUTH ONCE KNOWN TO MAN, FOR MAN'S WELFARE, EVER HAS BEEN DESTROYED OR DEFEATED, because of selfishness and greed of ulterior interests who think LESS OF IT and MORE OF THEIR DOLLAR INCOME, SACRIFICING MANKIND TO GET IT.

That "God" of the Universe which always has been, has spoken thru MANY tongues, MANY languages; worshipped in MANY forms; written about in MANY books; interpreted in MANY ways by MANY consecrated men and women. But no greater has been proven than when MAN HIMSELF proved the existence of A LIVING "GOD" **IN LIVING** MAN by making it possible for that everlasting "God" to become a tangible, seeable, existing reality **IN** MAN. In this sense, Chiropractic is almost a LIVING "GOD"-like religion IN MAN which no man has any right to TRY TO CAST OUT OF MAN, OR TO SAY THAT "GOD" IN MAN "MUST GO," merely because some are so blind they can't see, so deaf they won't hear, so insensible they can't sense its greatness IN man as a living entity.

On God in the Tissues

v. 37 1961 The Glory of Going On (pp. 247)

This also is true of man. What good and of what value are all the brains, stomachs, livers, bowels, muscles, bones, and what have you, in single or multiple systematized locations of organic physical structures of a human being? What is the delivery and performance of any or all of these, UNLESS THERE IS AN ABSTRACT SPIRIT, SOUL, EGO, PERSONALITY, INNATE INTELLIGENCE, OR "GOD" flowing into and thru all material structures to generate an intelligent direct action to PROduce LIFE...

Little did D. D. Palmer know that when he liberated that INNATE SPARK in Harvey Lillard, which restored his hearing, he was to stir up a hornets' nest as to the righteousness of that principle within his own family of followers; nor did he understand the breadth, length, and depth of how or why HE was to originate a NEW premise in the world of man's philosophies, sciences, and arts of an abstract, distant, and yet so near UNIVERSAL "GOD" IN WHICH MILLIONS PLACED THEIR HOPES, ASPIRATIONS, AND BY SO DOING MADE THE "GOD" OF THE UNIVERSE A LIVING, REAL, TANGIBLE "GOD" **IN** MAN, which FLOWED DOWNWARD **IN** MAN, WORKED **IN** MAN, WHICH WAS NO LONGER A HOPED FOR IDEAL BUT BECAME A WORKABLE, PRACTICAL, ACTUAL, AND REALISTIC KNOWLEDGE WHICH COULD

BE DEPENDED UPON TO **REPRODUCE** LIFE, **PERPETUATE** LIFE, AND **PROLONG** LIFE, IF, AS, AND WHEN PEOPLE GOT SICK.

His successor who, by right of inheritancy, formulated THIS LAW OF LIFE into consciousness in the minds of man, presented its postulates, methods of sources and expressions. He presented in millions of sick tangible proof of the correctness of those deductions.

On Living God in Living Man

v. 37 1961 The Glory of Going On (pp. 251-253)

It is so closely knitted into the composition of living man that every living person, everywhere, can look into the mirror and see and understand there IS A LIVING "GOD" WITHIN HIM that flows from ABOVE-DOWN, INSIDE-OUT, which will get him well if sick, make him a better man in his relationship to IT.

Be your beliefs and faiths what they are, under whatever title you think best, what better is there than to have LIVING proof of a LIVING "God" WITHIN you, ALWAYS present, NEVER absent; READY, WILLING, ANXIOUS, DESIRING to relieve you of aches and pains, prolong life to its full span, to make existence more pleasant, harmonious, which will place YOU in coordination with ITself; which is within you IN SUPER-ABUNDANCE IF it can get thru obstructions, impediments which exist between it and your body.

Every Chiropractor, whether he realizes it or not, every time he corrects the impediment between the living "GOD" in man, IS AN APOSTLE of that living "God," bringing into reality the Living Intellectual "God" from above, permitting it to work thru the living material bodies of all mankind. IT IS A LIVING PROVABLE "GOD" IN MAN, THE VERY SOUL AND LAW OF HIS BEING.

What greater joy hath man than to know he is making possible an explanation of the Superior "God" into a Living Human "God!"

because of WHAT he does, AS he does it, WHEN he does it, to get sick people well.

Our Chiropractic philosophy is a natural and normal inter-pretation of AN ETERNAL Law of Life. It brings directly into consciousness a new and better method of living; to you, yours, and your children; a LIVING "GOD" inside you, working FOR you, WITH you—every year, day, hour, minute, and second—keeping you alive and healthy when sick, responding to your every human demand and need, WITHOUT WHICH YOU WOULD NOT BE.

Your concept of it does not and cannot change its reality. What you believe outside and above that, may be for your spiritual benefit; but this LAW OF LIFE is a NEED TO LIVE, without which you would cease to be. That law WILL live IN man in spite of SOME men, not because of them. No man or set of men can drive that "ONE CAUSE—ONE CURE" law of life OUT of man That "MUST" NOT "GO." It's THERE; it HAS BEEN THERE; and it's THERE TO STAY!

It is the one GREAT "ONE CAUSE—ONE CURE" for all ills of the soul, spirit, mind, and body. WHAT MORE COULD MAN ASK FOR, WANT, OR NEED? That "God"-given, freely-given LAW OF LIFE will protect and defend ITSELF as it personifies itself thru men and women who HAVE a clear, clean-cut KNOWLEDGE of that "God"-given, free flow law FROM ABOVE-DOWN, INSIDE-OUT, WITHIN themselves, being exemplified in them in their daily work, saving the "God"-life law in others.

The value TO mankind of that "God"-LAW **IN** man depends upon how well man permits that "God"-law IN man to express itself, and how much he utilizes that LAW OF LIFE to become A LAW OF EVERY DAY ACTION in himself AND IN OTHERS, wherein he aims to liberate THAT LAW in himself as well as in others.

Time ALWAYS has and ALWAYS WILL perpetuate those methods which better serve mankind. CHIROPRACTIC IS NO

EXCEPTION TO THAT RULE. Our illustrious father placed this Chiropractic trust in OUR keeping, to keep it pure and not sullied or defamed. We pass it on to you unstained, to protect as he would also have you do. As he passed on, so will we. We admonish you to keep this principle and practice unadulterated and unmixed. Humanity needed THEN what he gave us. You need what we NOW give you. Out there in those great open spaces are multitudes seeking what YOU possess.

Ayuthia, Thailand (B.J. at base)

The burdens are heavy; responsibilities are many; obligations are providential; but the satisfaction of traveling the populated highways and byways relieving suffering, prolonging lives, adding millions of years to lives of millions of suffering people, will bring forth satisfactions and glories with greater blessings than you think. Time is of the essence. May God flow from ABOVE-DOWN His bounteous strengths, courages, and understandings to carry on; and may your Innates receive and act on that free flow of wisdom from ABOVE-DOWN, INSIDE-OUT; for you HAVE in YOUR possession a sacred trust. Guard it well.

Appendix
Our Chiropractic Commandments

B.J. Palmer's spirituality was very practical. It would not be a balanced presentation without at least including the chiropractic commandments. When it comes to actually being a chiropractor, as B.J. puts it, "All else is excess baggage! Nothing else is of importance!"

v. 38 1961 The Great Divide (pp. 14-15)

OUR CHIROPRACTIC COMMANDMENTS

1. INNATE INTELLIGENCE: the creator, director, controller, builder, organizer.

2. THE HUMAN BEING: a structure; the *created* object; the builder production.

3. POWER and/or energy plus organized matter, equals organized motion.

4. INTELLIGENT POWER and/or energy, plus intelligently organized matter, equals intelligent organized life.

5. INNATE INTELLIGENCE POWER and/or energy FLOWS FROM brain TO body THROUGH nerves.

6. MENTAL IMPULSE SUPPLY FLOWS THROUGH at a definite quantity and quality, per a definite rate of speed, per a definite unit of time, known only to INNATE.

7. If NORMAL quantity and quality flows through at a NORMAL rate of speed, per a normal unit of time—health.

8. If normal quantity and quality flows REDUCED because par to a LOWERED quantity and quality, it LOWERS and SLOWS normal rate of speed of tissue cellular motion, Reduces and slows speed of action of motion of structural matter—dis-ease.

9. REDUCED QUANTITY of nerve force flow reduces rate of speed of action OF FUNCTION dis-ease.

10. REDUCED SPEED of action per unit of time reduces the product and/or by-products of action which, being an integral part of a whole, disturbs and unsettles every other product or by-product of which it is a part.

ll. This upset of one part upsets many other parts adaptively, hence creating direct and indirect symptoms and pathologies, called objective and subjective, usually the indirect, subjective or adaptive conditions being more pronounced become the main observation in diagnosis, overlooking the primary and making prominent the secondaries.

12. There is but ONE dis-ease, regardless.

13. LACK of energy flow, Lack of motion of matter, Lack of function is dis-ease.

14. That which APPEARS to be INCREASED function is natural adaptative process to LACK OF normal function.

15. Dis-ease is UNBALANCED RELATIONSHIP between Innate Intelligence and function, normal and abnormal rate of motion; per units of time involved.

16. Intelligence, being eternal and abstract, cannot be unbalanced.

17. Time, being eternal and abstract, cannot be unbalanced.

18. Matter, per se, CAN be unbalanced in relationship with other two.

19. Vertebral subluxation, at occipito-atlantal-axial area, is THE PLACE where matter can distort matter to where it distorts the triune relationship.

20. Vertebral subluxation *occludes* inter-vertebral or spinal fora-men opening, *produces* pressures upon nerves, INTERFERES with and offers RESISTANCE to normal quality flow of In-nate power or energy enroute from and between any and all parts of brain to any and all parts of body.

21. Vertebral subluxation is the valve, the switch button, which, turned OFF makes well people sick; turned ON makes sick people well.

22. Vertebral subluxation, ADJUSTED, *opens* occlusions, *releases* pressures, *permits* a normal RESTORATION of normal quantity and quality flow of Innate mental impulse supply between Innate function, brain and body; reestablishes a nor-mal rate of action of matter, per a unit of time—health.

23. When this IS accomplished, perfect relationship and balance between Innate, matter and time have been attained—health.

24. The Chiropractic principle and practice being correct—to know Innate, to know vertebral subluxation, to KNOW HOW to adjust correctly, are what make a Chiropractor.

25. All else is excess baggage! Nothing else is of importance!

Epilogue: B.J. Palmer's Post-formal Development

Introduction

The chiropractic profession has a long history of eclectic personalities, dynamic egos, polarized conflicts, and leading edge philosophies of health and healing. No one person typifies this history better than Joshua Bartlett Palmer (1881-1961), known to his friends, students, and followers as B.J.

Palmer's influence on the development of the chiropractic profession was profound. After taking over the fledgling Palmer school from his father in 1904, with about 50 students, he grew the profession to 30,000 chiropractors in twenty years, and wrote 32 books over the course of his life. During the first seventy-five years of the profession, 75% of all chiropractors were Palmer graduates (Keating, 1997). Today there are 70,000 chiropractors worldwide, 20,000 chiropractic students, and millions of patients past and present. It is the largest health profession besides medicine and dentistry.

Most examinations of Palmer's life have been biased in one form or other. Whether written by his staunchest supporters and disciples (Dye, 1939; Maynard, 1982) or by rationalistic historiographers (Keating, 1997; Gaucher-Peslherbe, 1993), or by his son (Palmer, 1967), no study to date has systematically examined Palmer from the perspective of post-formal development. This author hopes to do so and thereby place Palmer's life in a framework truly worthy of his legacy. And there lies my bias; to bring forth aspects of Palmer's life so as to acknowledge his significant spiritual insights and thus, to better understand the development of chiropractic as a profession largely influenced by post-formal thinking.

Post-formal development is a relatively new concept in the history of psychology. Its most basic position is that the adult does not stop their development once formal-logical thinking develops. According to Piaget, the formal operational stage is the height of human development. As we will see, other researchers such as Beck, Cook-Greuter, Wade, and Wilber suggest otherwise. Those researchers have shown that there are several levels of development that have been studied and verified cross-culturally that go beyond Piaget's formal operations. Palmer is an excellent example of this type of development.

First I will discuss the main levels of development according to the various theorists, and then examine the difference between stages of consciousness, states of awareness and lines of development. This will set the stage for a rudimentary examination of Palmer's life, both his most life changing moments, his achievements, as well as his writings. Palmer's life and writings will be discussed in conjunction with the various stages of development. In this way a case will be made that through his writings and actions Palmer developed through many of the stages including some of the highest ones. His views on religion and spirituality will be one way to track the development of his sense of self throughout his writings.

It is difficult to convey the complexity of the life of such a man in a short essay. Thus, only the highlights, pivotal events, and to my understanding, greatest awakenings will be presented.

This essay has been undertaken in hopes of vindicating Palmer as a very advanced soul who has been largely misunderstood because his level of awareness and daily cognition were far ahead of his time. A biographical and scholarly examination is the best way to determine just where he was on the spectrum of human consciousness. For this reason, much of the essay will be a historical story filled with direct quotes from Palmer and his biographers.

The hypothesis of this paper is that B.J. Palmer's life was punctuated by peak experiences and transient states which developed into permanent traits and realizations. The higher stages that he developed into in his later years were accessed throughout his life by his constant quest for the essence of the chiropractic adjustment. To him, the chiropractic adjustment of the vertebral subluxation released pressure on the nervous system and allowed the individual to open to the innate intelligence both in health and in mind and spirit. This type of opening was to Palmer a doorway to the universal intelligence or God.

An Abridged Overview of Integral Psychology

Wilber has mapped out a "fifth force" in psychology: *integral psychology*. It is based on a combination of theoretical models. The most basic way of interpreting integral psychology is through the ladder-like modeling of human development (all levels). Added to this is a method of analysis that includes intentional, observable, theoretical, and communal components to experience. In this way, human development can be viewed in a stage-like pattern that does not end at rational scientific thought or Piaget's formal operations. Human consciousness has been shown to develop well into adulthood. Also, this development can be seen in all four quadrants of development (described below as *All Quadrant All Level* or *AQAL*).

Why AQAL?

Wilber's method of analysis provides a comprehensive map through which to analyze any useful system or model of healing or in this case individual consciousness (Wilber, 1995). It is comprehensive because it includes, body, mind, heart, soul, and spirit, scientific observation, objective theory, cultural and social contexts, as well as internal subjective experience.

The AQAL (pronounced "A-quil") approach has been used in examining several areas of inquiry, including the philosophy of health, medicine and Palmer's model of consciousness (Astin and Astin, 2002; Senzon, 2000). By applying this method to Palmer's life, we can see whether his development of self was complete.

First it will be important to define AQAL in a very rudimentary fashion. It will then be applied to Palmer's life in all of its complexity. Thus while examining Palmer's development through the levels of consciousness, which includes his period of scientific inquiry, we can explore his philosophical conceptions, as well as his communal and cultural accomplishments. So, at the end of each section on Palmer's stages, there will be a small discussion about the development of the lower quadrants. As Wilber has noted, in true development also considered evolution; we "tetra-evolve," meaning, all four quadrants at once (Wilber, 2000).

All Quadrants

All quadrants, refers to a grid approach to knowledge and experience. It can be explained by drawing a simple four-quadrant grid in the form of a plus sign. In the upper right quadrant (UR) is placed scientific observations such as the clinical observations of the chiropractor, what Wilber calls "it." In the lower right quadrant (LR) is placed theoretical models about reality, such as dynamical systems theory, complexity theory, as well as philosophy. This is what Wilber calls "IT" (capitalized to differentiate the observations of matter and life (it), from

138

the explanatory frameworks (IT)). Both UR and LR are objective by nature. The upper left quadrant (UL) is for internal and subjective experience, such as emotional states, physiological feelings, as well as spiritual experiences and states and stages of consciousness. Wilber calls this quadrant "I." The lower left quadrant (LL) is relegated to cultural experience, such as religion, communal gatherings, healing retreats, etc. Wilber calls this quadrant "We." The four quadrants can be broken down into "I," "We," and "It." (Please see figures 1-4)

All Level

All Level refers to the various levels of consciousness that an individual or society as a whole could achieve. For our purposes, this paper will mostly focus on the individual; namely B.J. Palmer.

Developmental Models

Within this framework, several models will be useful, such as those by, Beck and Cowan, Wade, Cook-Greuter and Piaget. Each of these theorists has provided a stage-like model of the self's development from the very earliest stages of human development through some of the higher levels. Table 1 below shows some of their models and how they correlate. Beck and Cowan's Spiral Dynamics, Wade's Holonomic Theory of Consciousness, and Cook-Greuter's model of ego-development will be used as the map. Beck and Cowan's model describes the development of values, Wade's describes personality development, Cook-Greuter describes the self, and Piaget describe's cognitive development. Wilber integrates each of the models. For our purposes, the values level is sufficient to understand Palmer's development up through the *first tier*, Wade, Cook-Greuter, and Wilber will be used to describe the higher levels. (Beck and Cowan 1996; Ginsburg and Opper 1969; Cook-Greuter, 1990; Wade 1996; Wilber, 2000).

Spiral Dynamics was developed based on the research of Clare Graves of a small sample of individuals and has been tested in cross-cultural venues. Its basic schema is presented in Table 2. Each structure of consciousness is described as a value meme, or vMeme. A meme (pronounced "Mccm") is a value structure that is shared by an entire society. Each level represents the ontogenetic development of humanity as well as the phylogenetic development of each individual human. So,

Wilber	Beck and Cowan	Wade	Piaget
Archaic	Instinctive (Beige)	Reactive	Sensorimotor
Archaic/Magical			
Magical	Magical/ Animistic (Purple)	Naive	Preconceptual/ Preoperational
Magic/Mythic			Intuitive (Conceptual) Preoperational
Mythic/Mythic	Power Gods (Red)		Concrete Operational
Mythic/Rational	Absolutist Religious (Blue)	Conformist	Concrete Operational (2) (Conop to early formop)
Rational Formalism	Individualistic/ Achiever (Orange)	Achievement/ Affiliative	Formal Operational
Pluralistic Relativism	Relativistic (Green)	Affiliative/ Achievement	Late Formop
Holistic Integralism	Systematic Integrative (Yellow) Global Holistic (Turquoise)	Authentic	
Psychic	Coral		
Subtle		Transcendent	
Causal			
Non-dual		Unity	

Table 1 was compiled from Wilber (2000, p. 203-207). Wilber's earliest stages generally correspond to Piaget, his middle and upper stages span most other theorists.

each level represents an epoch of human history as well as a stage of individual human development. The color spectrum makes it very useful to delineate each structure of consciousness. Spiral Dynamics represents the core values of each structure, and thus is representative of the self in its most basic sense. The first six levels are considered *subsistence* levels of consciousness, the upper two and beyond are considered *being* levels. The jump from Green to Yellow is just as far as the jump from Beige to Green (Beck and Cowan, 1996). As noted above, when discussing the second tier or the *being* levels, other models will be used.

> Spiral Dynamics:
>
> **Beige**: Instinctual - 100,000 years ago.
> **Purple**: Magical - 50,000 years ago.
> **Red**: Power –10,000 years ago.
> **Blue**: Conventional –5,000 years ago
> **Orange**: Achievement/Rational –300 years ago
> **Green**: Sensitive, pluralistic, relativistic –150 years ago
> **Yellow**: Holistic - 50 years ago
> **Turquoise**: Integral - 30 years ago

Table 2: Spiral Dynamics; a brief overview of the value-line of development (ages and dates are only suggestive).

Wilber describes the spectrum of development as follows,

"Briefly, what I am proposing is that the psychology of the mature human being is an unfolding, emergent, oscillating spiraling process marked by progressive subordination of older, lower-order behavior systems to newer, higher-order systems as an individual's existential problems change...When the human is centralized in one state of existence (as I would put it, when the self's center of gravity hovers around a particular wave of consciousness) he or she has a psychology which is particular to that state. His or her feelings, motivations, ethics and values, biochemistry, degree of neurological activation, learning system, belief systems, conception of mental health, ideas as to what mental illness is and how it should be treated, conceptions of and preferences for management, education, economics, and political theory and practice are all appropriate to that state." (Wilber, 1999)

Wilber has correlated dozens of approaches that map out the various levels of consciousness. This is a central aspect to integral psychology, that the individual has the innate ability to develop through each level of consciousness, and that they do not need to stop their growth once adulthood begins. Exemplars of higher order development span the ranks of history from Buddha to Ramana Maharshi, from Jesus to Meister Eckart, from Mohammed to Rumi. Wilber also makes clear distinctions between states, stages, and lines of development (Wilber, 2000).

The Self: Lines, States, Structures

141

It is important to very clearly define our terms. Wilber has been instrumental in mapping the terrain in this field. He has synthesized many different researched models of subjective development, as well as the more metaphysical or traditionally spiritual levels, and emphasized the need to differentiate between the various lines of individual development such as cognitive, moral, aesthetic, etc. He has also discussed the need to differentiate between lines, states, and structures (Wilber, 1997). For example, an individual can exist in a very enlightened structure of psychological or postconventional consciousness, and still be lacking in moral development, or still be fixated on some narcissistic level, while experiencing ever-higher states of awareness. An individual is never fully embedded in a higher level of awareness until they have worked out much of the lower levels.

A structure of consciousness relates to the main levels of awareness that an individual exists at, the "center of gravity" of their self. This is often explained in terms of Piaget's cognitive levels of development; sensorimotor, preoperational, concrete operational, and formal operational. Other researchers have found evidence for postformop levels of development (Cook-Greuter, 1999; Loevinger, 1976). Wilber points to the higher levels of spiritual awareness as transrational levels, as the logical developmental sequence beyond Piaget's formop.

These levels that center around the self, are representative of only one line of development, the cognitive line. It appears that there are at least two-dozen lines of development such as values, moral, aesthetic, affective, interpersonal, artistic, etc. Most of these lines however follow the same sequence as the cognitive line so therefore the cognitive line is necessary but not sufficient for general development (Wilber, 2000).

Beyond lines and structures of consciousness are states. According to Wilber, states of consciousness come in two varieties: natural and altered. Natural states consist of waking, dreaming, and deep sleep. Altered states occur when an individual has an experience of one of the other states of consciousness, but it is not their "center of gravity." For example, an individual who exists mostly in a narcissistic mode of awareness can have an experience of a higher, more altruistic mode. The individual will not merge with the higher level unless all of their lines of development have been essentially completed.

Wilber writes,

142

"But all of those peak experiences, no matter how profound, are merely temporary, passing, transient states. In order for higher development to occur, those *temporary states must become permanent traits*. Higher development involves, in part, the conversion of altered states into permanent realizations. In other words, in the upper reaches of evolution, the transpersonal potentials that were only available in temporary states of consciousness are increasingly converted into enduring structures of consciousness (states into traits)." (2000, p. 15)

The Wilber-Combs matrix presents just this, that a person can achieve any state of altered consciousness from any level. There is a wide variety of combinations. I would suggest that due to Palmer's quest for the answer to innate intelligence, his daily meditative states were centered around nature mysticism. It was this constant attention toward that level of awareness that pulled him up through the spectrum of consciousness and eventually beyond that level (Combs 2002; Wilber, 2000).

Cook-Greuter writes, "On rare occasions, a transformation or vertical change occurs in response to persistent discrepancies that cannot be accommodated through horizontal integration or defensive mechanisms. In that case, the whole previous meaning system may be transformed and restructured into a new, more expansive and inclusive theory…which transforms or reorganizes the current meaning system into a higher order of integration." (1999, p. 33)

As the individual develops through the stages of consciousness according to each line, the new and emergent level is marked by the end of the previous level. Cook-Greuter notes that as the individual develops, the boundaries of that structure of consciousness begin to soften, then become permeable to the next level, and finally the individual stabilizes at the next "center of gravity" and new boundaries are established. This also occurs due to destabilizing instances in the self-system, the death of a loved one, loss, dramatic life changes, and crises.

B.J. Palmer's Life as a Model of Higher Development

The hypothesis of this paper is that Palmer systematically developed through most of the levels of consciousness. He may not have stabilized each line within every stage, but he may very well have developed his value line and possibly his self line stably into higher levels of conscious awareness. This cannot be measured in the strictest sense of the term, but it can be inferred from what we know about his life and his extensive writings.

In Palmer's case there could be a very highly developed line such as the "spiritual" line along with less developed lines, such as the interpersonal line. This could be seen as a less developed structural line. A fault such as that has often been used in the past to discredit Palmer as a person. Hopefully this analysis will do the opposite, it will show his most advanced forms of consciousness while also showing his humanity.

This form of stunted development at one line with advanced development of another is a very common type of psychopathology. The aim of integral psychology is to map out the many types of combinations of lines and stages in a psychograph, thereby giving the individual the benefits of utilizing different forms of therapy, meditation, exercises, etc., to develop all lines simultaneously. Included within integral, is also the full development of body, mind heart, soul and spirit. This limited exploration is just that, a look at Palmer's attempt to develop all of his lines into ever-higher stable structures of conscious experience.

A challenge to suggesting that Palmer's development went through specific periods is that many of his writings were written years after the events discussed. In this respect, the level of consciousness from which he recounted his life was usually several stages above the period that he wrote about.

Value Meme	Years
Red	1890s
Blue	1900-1924
Orange	1924-1936
Green	1936-1952
Yellow- Turquoise	1953-1955
Coral?	1957-1958
Transcendent?	1959-1961

Table 3: Palmer's life according to
Spiral Dynamics including year

Whether he developed into the yellow-meme or Second Tier between 1933-1938, or between 1948-1955 is not clear. His polarized approach to introducing the HIO technique in 1934 was probably based in the

144

orange-meme as well as the development of his million-dollar research clinic in 1935. Also, he wrote several books which represent the green-meme around 1950. As discussed below, Palmer's first writings that were written from the yellow-meme are from 1953. Thus it is probable that his transition to the *being* levels, or Second Tier was around 1953. A preliminary sketch of these time periods is mapped out in Table 3.

At this point, we will discuss Palmer's development starting in his early years and moving eventually toward his postformal development.

B.J. The Controversy

While discussing the many controversies that surrounded Palmer throughout his life, Keating writes, "There are chiropractors who swear by him, and those who swear at him." (p. vi) Palmer's life is surrounded by a mythos. Gaucher-Peslherbe wrote that B.J. was messianic in his zeal for chiropractic (1993). His own father D.D., referred to him as the "enveloper" rather than B.J.'s term, the "developer" of chiropractic (1910, p. 658).

At the same time, many Chiropractic Schools and several international professional organizations rally around him as an inspiration and teacher. And still, to most chiropractors, B.J. was an enigma. They know only what their "school" taught about him, or what others have said or written. Not many have actually read Palmer, and those few who have usually just skim the surface with one or two books. Between 1906-1917, he wrote nine books, between 1920-1944, he wrote seven, between 1949-1953, eight books, and 1955-1961, another eight!

We can use these books as a guide to Palmer to find out what he thought, and how he developed over time. Many of the arguments against Palmer have to do with his early deeds or writings, and may have no bearing on his last decades. This type of analysis is just the beginning. It is a way to make sense of the complicated history of chiropractic and healing in America in the twentieth century.

Palmer polarized many people throughout his years as leader of the profession. The question is; which level of consciousness was he at during each of these major incidents? If Palmer was teaching and developing chiropractic from higher levels of development than his students and colleagues, then it stands to reason that he was misunderstood. Often Palmer's staunchest critics are speaking from one level of consciousness without understanding Palmer, because he was in a higher level. A discussion of this type of criticism across tiers of development will be made later. For now, Palmer's first tier of development will be discussed.

Palmer's Early Years (Red)

Our story begins with Palmer's writings about his childhood. He recounts in book after book how his family life as a child was very difficult. He spent much time living on the streets and confronting a very demanding father, Daniel David Palmer (D.D.), founder of chiropractic (Maynard, 1982), and an even more difficult step-mother (Keating, 1997).

His father D. D. Palmer was married four times. He started as a school teacher and then a grocer. He eventually studied magnetic healing and was an avid student of spiritualism, Confucianism, and science, especially medical textbooks (Gielow, 1981; Peterson and Weiss, 1995). As a father however, he was hard. In one story, B.J. recounts how his father stormed into the schoolhouse to demand that his daughter return home to clean the chamber pots at the clinic, a daily chore. The young girl was mortified that her father made this announcement in front of her class (Maynard, 1982).

B.J.'s attempts to escape his family life and poverty were through sensory pleasures. This next quote is also used by Keating to demonstrate B.J.'s days as a juvenile delinquent. Palmer wrote that he was,

"a mental derelict, a no-account kid bum. We (B.J.) spent our mental and physical sap pursuing false pleasures. We were one worthless hulk of degenerate boy. We were a cross-section example of the sexual delinquent of that era. Between five and fifteen, we were confirmed and habitual sex-drunkard, dead drunk in the sexual gutter…We had not yet learned that masturbation was the thief of brain food which destroyed mental values." (1950b, p. 87)

I have included the above quote with much trepidation. It is a delicate matter when subjects such as these enter a mainstream publication. I used this specific quote for two reasons. The first was that, since it has already been used by Keating, I felt that it would be more useful seen in the larger context of Palmer's topic in that specific essay (which

146

continues in the next section), and the context of Palmer's development, because this telling remark gives us a great deal of information about him. The most obvious was that he had not yet developed his faculties of restraint and concentration. More about this will be discussed in the next section as well.

The less obvious is this topic of semen retention and its relationship to "brain food." There is a great deal of literature across many cultures, and martial art forms that consider the excessive release of semen to be a depletion of "chi" or life force, energy. Most of the writings on this subject are written from the second or third tier. (Reid, 1992; Chia and Winn, 1995; David Deida, 1999) Palmer did not write that statement until 1950, when he was 69 years old, already moving into the second tier.

Palmer himself prefaced the above statement with, "We will be criticized for this story, because it will reveal one tabu subject which polite society does not talk about, but which everybody knows exists. If this story is to do anybody any good, example must be told as it was." (1950b, p. 87)

Between five and fifteen was Palmer's sojourn in the red-meme and the beginning of his development into the blue-meme (which will be discussed next). B.J. did not finish high school. As one story goes, he was kicked out for setting the white mice free (Maynard, 1982). Another biographer states that Palmer had to stop going to school for financial reasons. He had to go to work (Dye, 1939). After a few years at various jobs, he went on tour with a vaudeville troupe, practicing as a hypnotic patient in a show. This was from around ages 17-20.

According to Beck, the red-meme/Power–Gods is a standard level for young children. It also has a direct relationship to street gangs. It seems like B.J. at this point in his life was very Red. This level has also been called egocentric. It is defined as the "self against the world." It is also the level of anti-social behavior and lying (Wade 1996; Beck and Cowan 1996; Wilber 2000).

It is important to fully develop in each level before an individual can completely transform to the next. As the growth through each level progresses in a healthy way the skills and behaviors mastered at each level become working protocols to deal with the challenges of life. Also, a person can enter into the next level without fully developing all lines from each level below (Wilber, 2000). This is probably B.J.'s case, even though he reached very high levels of spiritual awareness among other lines, still, he was not perfect.

To sum up Palmer's early development according to the four quadrants: all that can be noted for his development in the lower left quadrant, or social/cultural relationships is; his self-described leadership of a street gang, his dysfunctional family life, and his very early development of libido. As for his upper and lower right quadrant, or objective observational and theoretical developments, nothing much can be noted. As for his upper left quadrant or subjective internal experience, he was mostly egocentric or situated within the red-meme during this period.

Hypnosis and Transformation

Michael Murphy has noted that hypnotic suggestion is not generally considered to be a transformative practice such as martial arts or Buddhist meditation, or Christian prayer, but it does stimulate an individual's capacity for, "creative absorption, perceptual flexibility, hypermnesia, exceptional physiological control, psychosomatic plasticity, and access to subliminal levels of consciousness." (p. 348) According to Lerner, during the years 1899-1901, Palmer was a subject in a hypnotist's vaudeville act (Keating, 1997). Further research is necessary to explore this hypothesis, but it is possible that he was immersed in hypnotic states on a daily or weekly basis for months or possibly years at a time. This lends great insight into his future development of self as well as the development of his teachings.

Murphy writes, "This, perhaps, is the most fundamental insight we gain from hypnosis, this glimpse of a superior intelligence within us that can drastically alter our perceptions and thinking, restore healthy functioning, and enhance our most basic capacities. From the wealth of mesmeric and hypnotic phenomena we learn that human functioning can be developed in dramatic ways by evoking something that resembles Frederic Myers's 'subliminal mind'." (1994, p. 348)

I would suggest that Palmer's days with the vaudeville show as a hypnotic subject, may have immersed the young man into transient higher states of consciousness. This same time period during which his father was developing the new philosophy that would dramatically transform B.J.'s mission in life and define who he was, was also the time that he spent in regular altered states of consciousness. These two things combined had an intense effect on Palmer's later growth and transformation.

B.J. wrote that Herbert L. Flint was a friend of his father D.D.'s. Whenever Flint came through town for his three-week stints, D.D. would invite him over for tea. B.J. wrote,

"Whether or not they discussed us and our 'sins' of omission or commission, we do not know, but we do know that Flint urged us to come on the stage to be tested as a subject. He did not encourage other boys of our gang. Flint could do nothing with us. We had no mentality to concentrate on his suggestions." (1950b, p. 90)

He claimed that he was at first a poor hypnotic subject for Flint's three-week stints in the Davenport area, three years in a row. Then Palmer went on tour with him for two seasons where he became an excellent hypnotic subject. Palmer wrote,

"We (B.J.) were his subject, when he broke a four-hundred pound rock on our chest, being suspended with shoulders on back of one chair, our ankles on back of another. We were his ace-in-the-hole subject for varied tests to demonstrate value of hypnosis." (1950b, p. 91)

Palmer also notes that he learned the art of self-hypnosis. And, that the art of being a good hypnotic subject was intense concentration. He allowed himself to be influenced by the positive hypnotic suggestions so that he could let go of his "derelict" ways. And also, that this was a turning point in his life, which laid the foundation for the mould of his life.

This is not the only analysis to suggest the great influence that the hypnotic trances had on Palmer. Lerner interviewed one of Palmer's deans Herbert Hender in the 1950's. Lerner wrote,

"I had the occasion to review this also with Dr. Herbert Hender... He recognized that I was touching the true B.J. when I brought up the subject of the 'post-hypnotic personality' that I believed B.J. had developed... All of the secondary personalities which B.J. has revealed to the outside world have in all probability been created by the hypnotic influences he was subject to more than 50 years ago and to the hypnotic attitudes he has allowed himself to practice since then..." (cited in Keating, 1997, p. 15)

Others have suggested that this period of Palmer's life was when he learned showmanship, lecturing, and role-playing (Dye 1939; Keating 1997). I suggest it was the beginning of his lifetime of spiritual awakening.

At age 17, his father was busy developing the philosophy and art of chiropractic. In several instances, Palmer explained that at age 17, 18, and 19, he "found himself" (Palmer, 1949, p. xix; 1950b, p. 65; 1952, p. 79; 1961a, p. 56; 1961c, p. 116). Palmer wrote,

"At seventeen, he (B.J.) 'found himself.' This boy had no education. Educationally, as the world understands it, he was far short. Innately, he had the wisdom of the ages working for him, with him." (1949, p. xix)

When an individual is constantly immersed in higher levels of consciousness, those levels act as a magnet that pull the individual higher (Washburn, 1988). This ability to access the subliminal mind would become one of Palmer's greatest gifts for himself and the profession.

B.J. Palmer the Conformist/Conventional (Blue)

In the next period of Palmer's life, he is greatly influenced by his father. According to B.J. he started calling himself doctor at age 17, grew a goatee and traveled to care for the sick. (Please note that the original quotes from Palmer include terminology and language, such as, "ourself" and "thot," not common to modern English language and the author has left them to preserve the historical tone of the quotes.)

Palmer wrote,

"Day after day, week after week, month after month, we listened to D. D. propound ideas. We drank them in, hungrily. In time, they percolated and we became saturated with their value. In time, we "found ourself", all of which has been written in various of our publications.

In 1902, D. D. Palmer issued us a diploma signed by himself, his wife, and ourself. We practiced Chiropractic since we were seventeen, calling ourself "Doctor." That was the why and wherefore of mustache and beard—to appear older than our years. We thot we could disguise youth because sick people did not want to go to a boy with a new idea they knew nothing about. We practiced in those early years in Lake City, Iowa; Traverse City and Manistique, Michigan; Elkins, Belington, and Kernes, West Virginia, etc." (1950b, p. 65)

Keating would disagree that Palmer acted as a chiropractor at age 17. To him, all that Palmer did during those years was to travel with the vaudeville show and was not to learn chiropractic for several years. The argument is thus presented, that Palmer invented his past in order to gain more authority over the chiropractic profession (Keating, 1997). There is evidence that he was on the road with the show, whether or not he acted as a chiropractor during that time is open to interpretation. I disagree with Keating, and choose to believe Palmer's assessment of his early life. At least in regards to the development of his own consciousness and his actions.

The conformist or blue-meme is the beginning of Piaget's formal operations. Here is where the individual seeks to fit into the society they are embedded in and develops a rigid value system as to right and wrong, good and bad. According to Wade, the limbic system, which governs the emotions, dominates this level of consciousness. It is also characterized by rationalization, quasi logic, and logical inconsistencies. Science is valued but only to support the truth (Wade, 1996). In this *conventional stage*, the individual is most interested in the "in-group," such as friends and family. Those who are outside of the group are rejected (Cook-Greuter, 1990).

The Transpersonal school of psychology views this stage as the consolidation of the ego's strength. As the ego develops in this stage, it grows farther away from things spiritual and is more involved in its own mental constructs. There is also an alienation from the body. This level of consciousness is very difficult to break away from (Wade, 1996).

As noted in the introduction, at this period of Palmer's life, he took over the school from his father in 1904. He then proceeded to get married and have a son, David Daniel Palmer. The school soon grew from about 50 students to 700 by 1911, about 1200 students by 1919, and 3,000 students by 1921 (Keating, 1997). Of this time period, Gibbons wrote,

"By 1910 B.J. was a man of property, owner of one the finest mansions on the top of Brady Street hill. He was the president of an institution

151

with more than 300 students, called himself a doctor and was already an editor and an author. He had married the daughter of a respected family, wore a Van Dyke beard and dressed in a fitting role for the leader of a professional body, a scholar and an academic." (1987, p. 10)

The biggest conformism as to chiropractic, was the establishment of the school, the constant need to determine the proper methods of chiropractic and to discredit heretical notions (Palmer, 1911, 1920), and the development of a professional organization, The Universal Chiropractors Association (Wardwell, 1992). Palmer even joined the first chiropractic fraternity, Delta Sigma Chi on November 6, 1913, of which he was made Honorary President. He also initiated chiropractic textbooks "the green books," that incorporated the philosophical premise that the body had an innate intelligence into standard science and physiology. He was building a community as well as a profession.

Keating writes,

"The early Palmer green books are filled with illustrations of the Developer's (B.J.'s) efforts to systematize the knowledge he had accumulated and to share this with the field. This writer knows of no other comparable work among chiropractors in this period." (p. 67)

The codification of the philosophy and the statues in the domain of law were a very important aspect of this era. Rehm has suggested that the need to defend chiropractors in court was when the philosophy of chiropractic actually began. It had to be proven that chiropractic was separate and distinct from medicine. This was initiated by Palmer's lawyer, Tom Morris in 1907, and perhaps inspired by some of D.D. Palmer's early students Solon Langworthy, Oakley Smith, and Minora Paxson, who wrote the first chiropractic textbook, *Modernized Chiropractic* in 1906 (Rehm, 1986; Holmes, 1924). By 1929, Morris supervised the defense of 3,300 chiropractors, and won 85-90% of the cases (Keating, 1997).

Palmer's introduction of the x-ray unit in 1909 as part of the chiropractic analysis lost him many followers. Some even left and started a new school, Universal Chiropractic College in 1910 (Keating, 1997). This was one of the first real disruptions. It was probably caused by his transformation from the blue-meme to the orange-meme, from conformist to non-conformist. His need to use science to prove the theories of chiropractic was to become a guiding value.

152

Upper Left Quadrant	Upper Right Quadrant
Blue/Conformist	• Use of x-rays in the analysis of the spine • Development of a chiropractic method called the Meric System, based on "nerve-tracing," • Refinement of techniques for chiropractic adjusting.
Lower Left Quadrant	**Lower Right Quadrant**
• Taking over of the chiropractic school • Establishing a curriculum • Growing the school • Creating a chiropractic community • Establishing of legal statutes • Starting a printing press in 1916 • Getting married • Having a child • Purchasing a home	• Revision of the philosophy • Creation of the new "green books" (science and chiropractic texts based on philosophy) • The use of quasi-logic

Figure 1: Palmer's Tetra-Evolution; blue-meme.

Each of these significant incidents reached an apex in 1913, with the death of his father D.D. Palmer. These crises caused enough friction and softening of boundaries to break B.J. out of the conformist stage, utilize his red non-conventional base, and explode into orange as a very successful entrepreneur and scientifically minded researcher.

Palmer's conformist period can be summed up according to quadrant as follows (see figure 1); the lower left quadrant is represented by his taking over of the chiropractic school, and establishing a curriculum, growing the school and the chiropractic community, becoming heavily involved in legal battles, starting a printing press in 1916, and getting married, having a child and purchasing a home. He developed the upper right quadrant through the use of x-rays in the analysis of the spine, a chiropractic method based on "nerve-tracing," and the refinement of

153

techniques for chiropractic adjusting. The lower right quadrant was developed through the philosophy within the new "green books," especially his revision of the 1906 text *The Science of Chiropractic: Its Principles and Adjustments*, coauthored by his father. In the 1910 edition, *The Science of Chiropractic: Its Principles and Philosophies*, he was the sole author, and many of the new ideas developed because of the court cases were incorporated (Wardwell, 1992; Wiese and Lykins, 1986). The upper left quadrant was conformist and conventional.

Entrepreneur Emerging (Orange)

The next stage is called the *conscientious stage* by Cook-Greuter. In this stage, she writes, "individuals are interested in reasons, causes, goals, costs, consequences, and the effective use of time. Formal operations and abstract rationality are at their peak. There is a deep belief in progress and the perfectibility of humankind. There is also a conviction that the proper analytical, scientific methods will eventually lead to the discovery of how things really are, that is, to the discovery of truth." (1990, p. 88)

While in each level of consciousness, Palmer constantly reached out to higher states of consciousness, which eventually pulled him to the next successive level. For example, during his blue conventional stage of establishing the school, the philosophy, the law statutes, and his family, he was learning the tools necessary for being a successful entrepreneur.

From the time that he became the president of the Palmer School of Chiropractic in 1906 to the opening of his research clinic in 1935, he wrote fourteen books, started a printing press, taught classes around the country and the world, and grew his school and chiropractic into a worldwide profession.

Wardwell wrote about Palmer's great skill as a salesman and motivational inspiration. He cites a visit to the Palmer campus in 1920 by Napoleon Hill, the famous author. According to Wardwell, Hill wrote of the experience,

"Here I found the most inspiring institution of any kind – bar none! – in America. Here I found MY teacher! A man who not only teaches about things, but how to do things. A man who embodies in his life and work

154

the principles of living and doing, the fine "Art of selling Yourself..."
(Wardwell, 1992, p. 71)

Palmer launched the first radio station west of the Mississippi in 1922
(WOC). By 1924, it was broadcasting at 5,000 watts, and was one of
the five strongest radio stations in the world. Ronald Reagan started his
broadcasting career under Palmer's tutelage. In 1930, Palmer expanded
to a second station in Des Moines, Iowa, (WHO). The primary purpose
for creating the stations was to advertise chiropractic. After the stock
market crashed in 1929, the radio stations became a very important
source of revenue for Palmer (Keating, 1997). Palmer even wrote one
book in 1942 entitled, *Radio Salesmanship: how its potential sales
percentage can be increased*. According to Palmer, this was a required
textbook in every radio station from New York to California for many
years (1949, p. 466).

Wade has suggested that this achievement stage looks like the
egocentric stage. This is a common misconception about B.J. He is
often depicted as entirely egocentric when in reality he was mastering
the orange-meme not through power but rationality. A quote from Dye,
who knew B.J., explains this very well,

"Since 1910 I have reported many a talk given by B.J. to his classes
and to public groups...In none of those that I have reported has B.J.
ever assumed an attitude that could be deemed autocratic or that could
be interpreted as an intimation that he would wreck the profession
unless it bowed to his dictates. Unfortunately, in the mannerisms used
by him in putting over an idea, he does get a little bit too emphatic with
the result the listener may have trouble in getting the entire idea...Even
the most casual member of the Pre-Lyceum or Lyceum Classes of 1936
and 1937 could not help getting the impression that B.J. was solely
interested in the continued evolution of the Chiropractic principle
toward a still more firm scientific foundation." (p. 291)

In regards to the four quadrants, Palmer again shows development in
every area (see figure 2). In the lower left quadrant he continues to
expand his message of health and healing to the masses through radio.
This is a cultural medium of exchange. He also used his great resources
to travel the world three times from 1921 to 1933. Also in this quadrant
is the creation of the B.J. Palmer Research Clinic. The Clinic itself
became a source of the culture that Palmer was creating. In the lower
right quadrant we can see a broadening of ideas, starting with green
book volume five, *The Philosophy of Chiropractic*, coauthored by John

155

Craven in 1916; the concepts of the cyclic interactions between the innate intelligence, the universal intelligence, and matter in the form of living bodies, is a pre-systems approach to health and healing. During this period as well, Palmer and his staff decided to rely on the philosophical method of deduction to base their theories upon. In the upper right quadrant, new instrumentation is developed to detect the vertebral subluxation, new chiropractic techniques are developed to deliver the chiropractic adjustment, and the research clinic. In the upper left quadrant, Palmer is rooted in the entrepreneurial/achievement stage of development.

Upper Left Quadrant	Upper Right Quadrant
Orange/Achievement	• Neurocalometer • Technique development: HIO • Research clinic formed
Lower Left Quadrant	Lower Right Quadrant
• Radio • World travel • Research clinic • Gardens	• Revision of the philosophy • Expansion of the "green books" • The use of deduction

Figure 2: Palmer's Tetra-Evolution; orange-meme.

Orange and Spirituality

This stage is marked by a heightened separation from the spiritual sense of awareness. It is important in this section to mention Palmer's impression of the mystics and yogis of India during his trip in 1925. He was very disillusioned by the poverty and the lack of cleanliness. He wrote;

"The glamour is gone. I have seen-I am glad to know. I came back to America more than ever pleased with the principles of Christ...the Fatherhood of God and the Brotherhood of Man, *as I interpret them* and continue living them as best I can." (1926, p. 363)

In this quote, we can see the transformation from the blue-meme to the orange-meme, and the disillusionment that will lead to the green-meme. The italics added by B.J. "as I interpret them," shows that he does not accept the conventions of organized religion. This use of the doctrine of the "Fatherhood of God and the Brotherhood of Man," Palmer eventually interprets as universal intelligence and the innate intelligence which connects all men. His outright disdain that he developed toward the "holy men" was very rationalistic which is characteristic of the orange-meme.

He wrote, "I have read books on India since I was a boy. I have read about the transmigration of souls, thot tranference, mind over matter, dissolution of soul and body, annihilation of space and time, etc…I have longed for the day that I would by contact, get it all direct…I went into it all and studied it thoroly; and again I was disillusioned. It is the cheapest and laziest tawdry way of becoming a dirty and filthy beggar in the name of religion, taking everything and giving nothing in return, that I have found in all my travels." (1926, p. 368)

This quotation is also important because, as we see Palmer's later development and his comments on Buddhism in 1953 and "Yogism" in 1958, his perspective is entirely changed. Besides being a wonderful example of the orange-meme, this quote as compared to the later ones on similar topics is just one example of the development of Palmer's self.

Crisis and Transformation 1920's

Several difficult incidents that were pivotal for B.J. helped him to transform from the orange-meme/achievement to the green-meme/sensitivity, and eventually to the second tier. For the 1920's however, Palmer was firmly rooted in the orange-meme.

The first incident was what has become known as the NCM Debacle (Wardwell, 1992). In 1924, B.J. introduced the Neurocalometer (NCM). This was a device designed to measure the heat of the spine in order to detect where there was a resistance to the nerve flow at the site of vertebral subluxation. Palmer's friend Dossa Evins designed the NCM after years of research.

In this one incident, we find the strength and weakness of the orange-meme, driven by a not-fully-developed blue-meme. B.J. sought to establish a truly objective means of detecting the mysterious vertebral subluxation. This, he honestly believed was the answer. Palmer wrote,

.

"Back in 1924 there was invented an instrument which was destined to change the methods used in Chiropractic; destined to change the approach and mental reasoning of Chiropractors to their sick patient's. It was destined to make possible discovery of the specific for the cause of dis-ease in the human body and to show accurately exact location of that cause. That instrument is the NEUROCALOMETER." (1961c, p. 89)

According to Keating, Palmer used this instrument to exert more control over the profession and to make a profit. Palmer told each chiropractor that they must lease one of these instruments from him. The price rose from $500 to $2,200 in less than a year. And, in the spirit of a not completely developed blue-meme, in no uncertain terms, he told them that if they did not use this instrument then they were not really practicing chiropractic. Subsequently he lost four of his core faculty who left the school in protest and started another school, Lincoln Chiropractic College. Today it is called National College (Keating, 1997).

Commenting on Palmer's attitude that all chiropractors will use the NCM whether they like or not, Dye interprets Palmer to mean that the scientific proof that the NCM will provide, will make the use of the instrument inevitable. Dye writes,

"It simply means, and can only mean, convinced as he is of the merit of the Neurocalometer, he is eventually going to prove to the profession that it will come to the use of the instrument, regardless of whether they accept or condemn it now. It can mean nothing else." (p. 284)

Maynard wrote that the stress was so overwhelming from the extensive criticism from the NCM debacle, that Palmer had a break down, and spent some time in a sanitarium called Pass Christian in Mississippi. He did not get the rest that he needed. In fact he spent most to the time in a bed dictating 100,000 words to a reporter. Palmer healed himself by building a gigantic garden in 1923-1924. He named it "A Little Bit O' Heaven."

He left Pass Christian and focused his attention on collecting glacial rocks and boulders by the ton from the banks of the Mississippi River. These were used to build the garden that was to boast two million visitors by 1959. B.J. consciously developed "A Little Bit O' Heaven" and the Buddhist Gardens as a "pilgrims retreat" of quiet and repose. Eventually, with the help of his grounds keeper Wilhelm Stahmer, the

158

garden was to contain waterfalls, shrubs, trees, ponds, as well as his dozens of statues of Buddhas, the pantheon of Hindu gods and many other things, all housed in a 3300 square foot building with a 40-foot ceiling (Palmer, 1949; Maynard, 1982). The initial building of this garden can be viewed as a two-year long meditation for Palmer that helped him to develop towards the next level.

Crisis and Transformation 1930's

As if he did not learn from the NCM debacle, in 1934 he introduced a new chiropractic technique, HIO (Hole In One) or Upper Cervical Specific. This new way of adjusting the spine was based on his research using his new instrument NCM. Again, he told the profession in no uncertain terms, if you are not doing HIO, then you are not a real chiropractor.

His standing in the profession declined because of these incidents. He still had a large and loyal following, but in the fringes of the profession, in other schools, and other states, his legacy was no longer the dominant chiropractic paradigm.

And then, in 1935, he opened the B.J. Palmer Research Clinic, at the time costing one million dollars to construct. This was the height of his rationalistic inquiry. Of this time period, Dye writes,

"Having known B.J. for many years, and having observed him in those years, I have noted a remarkable change within the past decade. Of course, as any man grows older in years he becomes more mellowed towards the events that cast difficulties in his path in earlier years. B.J. is no exception to this rule. On the other hand, he has not borne the animosities that so many of us carry to our final day. He has apparently become more tolerant toward his enemies in the field of Chiropractic, and has wrapped himself more and more in his research and experimental laboratories…" (1939, p. 293)

Unfortunately, due his lack of training in scientific investigation, his research is difficult to interpret. One thing that we do know of this time is that his research led him to studying the subtle energies of the body, and how the atmosphere and the environment had electrical effects on the organism in relation to the chiropractic adjustment and vertebral subluxation. His research is summed up in two books, *The Known Man or An Explanation of "the phenomena of life"* (1936), and *Chiropractic Clinical Controlled Research* (1951). This insight into the holistic

159

relationships within the organism, coupled with his studies of the world religions, his travels, and his constant quest for the answer to his questions about innate and universal, led him to the green-meme.

Green Unfolding...

The green-meme is marked by a critique of hierarchy and rationalism as well as an egalitarian outlook. In contrast, the yellow-meme, which is the beginning of the second tier is marked by an establishment of natural hierarchies and systems thinking. As noted above, incidents that weaken the individual's boundaries allow for them to more easily transform vertically to the next level.

At the height of these crises, B.J. traveled the world three times. In 1921-22 he, his wife Mabel, and son Dave traveled to China, Japan, and Korea. In 1924-25 they traveled to Thailand, Burma, Philippines, Singapore, India, Ceylon, Israel, Egypt, Arabia, Syria, Italy, Switzerland, France and England. In 1933, they traveled to Hawaii, Fiji, Samoa, New Zealand, Australia, Indonesia, and Cambodia. This is a pivotal and transitional time for Palmer. He grew in his sensitivity, his compassion, and his vision, as well as inspiration and spirituality. These journeys are recounted in two books, *Around the World with B.J.* (1926), and *Upside Down Inside Out with B.J.; Including The Greatest Mystery in History* (1953).

In his travel logs, we see several things happen for Palmer. The first is that his compassion and spirituality grow. He saw with his own eyes the poverty around the world. He also studied the world's religions and examined their main precepts. He traveled to their holy sites, shrines, and monasteries, and analyzed them through his own philosophical understanding that had been developing for these twenty years. He did not like everything that he saw, as mentioned above, but in retrospect, in his writings twenty-five years later, we can infer a profound transformation in Palmer's sense of self.

Palmer began to view religion as the striving of man to commune with the infinite. He referred to God as Universal Intelligence, and the soul within man as the innate intelligence, the divine spark of God. Innate was also seen to be the driving force behind the organization of the living form. While these concepts were inherited from his father, as his own spiritual development ensues, Palmer brings greater depth and insight into these ideas as he begins to embody them.

160

In his green postmodernist critique on religion in general, he focused many of his writings around Christianity. He condemned the idea that all people should be converted to one single belief. This is an excellent case in point. In 1926, during his travels abroad, he discussed missionary work in great detail. It is obvious that he had a distaste for it, but he does not condemn it outright. He merely suggested that it did not work very well. In 1950 however, he wrote extensively on the hypocrisy of the missionary ideal. (Palmer, 1926, 1950a)

While B.J. was criticizing organized religion in general, he also saw a common ground, that all people have the same life force, and this is the tie that binds all religions. He wrote, "Same health would be restored to a Buddhist, Mohammedan, Confusionist, Hindu, or whatever other religion he professed or denied." (1952, p. 87) Instead of the postmodernist critique of a dominator hierarchy, which should be toppled at all costs, he critiques and then replaces with a higher order of worldcentric beliefs that are centered on nature mysticism and even deity mysticism.

He also critiques modern science and medicine as too stuck in the rational perspective. The scientist or medical doctor that belonged to a religion and then proceeded to deny the body's innate intelligence through surgery and medications, to B.J., was a hypocrite. He wrote,

"This God-worshipper has been studying *physical* man four, eight, or ten years. He now begins to IMPROVE upon handiwork of God. Because this man has sat in a surgical pit for four years, he feels capable of saying—if actions speak louder than words —"God, you are ignorant. What do YOU know about making human beings? If you'd take a few lessons from surgeons, you'd make people according to OUR designs and leave our many 'useless' organs!" He makes a distinction between what he "believes" and gives money TO, and what he "knows" and takes money FOR." (1950a, p. 216)

This is again, at once a critique of the dominator hierarchy of medicine, science, law, religion, all in one, with a vision for a better way, an innate way, a more holistic way. The chiropractic adjustment which when given at the precise time and place, with "that special something," allows the body's inner wisdom to heal it, and allows the divine spark within to come forth to awareness. And this leads B.J. to the second tier, to the yellow-meme or the integrative perspective.

A discussion of the four quadrants is also possible for this level of Palmer's development (figure 3). In the lower left quadrant, he migrates to Sarasota, Florida, letting go of many of the responsibilities of leadership. Also, during this time period he wrote extensively. In the lower right quadrant, he applied his theories and insights to every domain of knowledge that he cared to mention. He wanted his philosophy to be universal and comprehensive truth. In the upper right quadrant, he completed his book Chiropractic Clinical Controlled Research in 1951, and described the research undertaken in the clinic to get people well and discover the one cure for all dis-ease. In the upper left quadrant, he opened to the possibility that all people have one common truth which lies within them as innate intelligence, and this became his internal experience. Also, he started to face his own failing health and eventual mortality.

Upper Left Quadrant	Upper Right Quadrant
Green/Sensitivity	• Chiropractic Clinical Controlled Research published.
Lower Left Quadrant	**Lower Right Quadrant**
• Semi-retirement in Sarasota, Fla. • Active proponent of the creation of the Barnum and Bailey Circus Museum.	• Green book volumes 22-28 written. • Development of the philosophy and its application across many domains of knowledge.

Figure 3: Palmer's Tetra-Evolution; green-meme.

Criticism Across Tiers

Jane Loevinger wrote, "In principle, a person does not fully understand the relevant thinking of people much above his or her own (level)." (Loevinger, as quoted in Cook-Greuter, 1999, p 140). And this brings us to the heart of Palmer's critics. Any discussion of criticism across tiers of development runs the risk of dismissing valid points as "not developed enough." Hopefully this will not be the case. However, much of the mythos that surrounds Palmer's life is based on this very paradox.

162

In an interview with the Shambhala Press about this topic as per his own critics, Ken Wilber writes, "Nothing much is gained by having different levels of consciousness attack each other." As difficult as this may seem, it is vitally important when examining Palmer's life. The interview continued discussing Wilber's book, *Sex Ecology and Spirituality* (SES),

"Shambhala: Okay, so this is starting to make more sense. When green critics read yellow sections in SES, they accuse you of being red-egocentric, arrogant, antispiritual, dominating, oppressive, controlling, etc."

"KW: Yes, that's right, but again, this doesn't mean that I am pure and am innocent of all of that. It just means that there are many second-tier (and third-tier) worldviews presented in SES, and the green-meme will in any event look at those and see nothing but the red meme." (Wilber, 2001)

Keating's critique of B.J. is a case in point. This is not to say that B.J. was a saint, he certainly was not. But if this developmental analysis is correct, and if B.J. achieved second or third tier consciousness, then much of Keating's criticism is just wrong. This would apply to several other authors as well, but the Keating quotes below are the easiest to use as an example.

Palmer's belief that his role was a manifestation of the divine, that his mission was to bring health and the god within to the masses of humanity, has been seen as messianic and egotistical. From the perspective of the third tier, this could be understood as a type of Bodhisattva vow. From the second tier, it could be seen as a highly developed sense of self fueled in part by an incompletely developed red-egocentrism, but not solely red by any means.

Keating writes, "he asserted his privilege to rule by virtue of birthright and commitment to true principle...like the divine right of kings, B.J.'s crown was a holy family mandate...Palmer's story is a tale of ego...B.J's philosophy of chiropractic became a celebration of self in several respects: a festival of egoism as well as egotism."
(1997, p. 273 & 275)

.

For his supporting evidence of this egoism, Keating uses Palmer's call to his followers to look within to the unlimited fountain of power and wisdom. When Palmer's writings are interpreted from the second or third tier, they are clearly written expositions on enlightenment and awakening, and as noted below, the developmental analysis of human capacities. They are not written from the red-meme, but from the yellow-meme, turquoise-meme, and coral-meme, or in Wade's terminology, authentic consciousness and transcendent consciousness.

The Second Tier

Research shows, that the second tier only makes up 2% of the adult population of America today, where for example, the green-meme is at about 20-25% (Cook-Greuter, 1999; Beck and Cowan, 1996).

I think that there are several factors that predisposed B.J. to opening to the second tier and beyond. The most obvious one is what I have termed the chiropractic Zen Koan, where his quest since age 17 was to discover the answer of innate intelligence, to listen to it, and grow into it, and eventually merge with it as the Universal Intelligence. Understanding the role of the chiropractic adjustment in that process was his constant transrational question (Senzon, 2000).

The second factor is his lifelong study of world religions, and especially Buddhism. From 1922 until 1933, B.J. studied all that he could about the people who built Ankor Wat in Cambodia. He also studied Buddhism and Hinduism in great detail throughout his life.

The third factor of his development into the second tier was his constant striving to perfect the art of chiropractic. When he developed HIO in 1934, he had been practicing and teaching the physical art of adjusting the spinal column for at least 30 years. Photos and videos of B.J. adjusting show that his entire body was engaged in every movement.

Dye noted, that in the student clinic at the Palmer School, 90% of the atlas adjustments from 1910 onwards that students could not do on their own, were performed by B.J. because of his "recognized skill." (Dye, 1939, p. 231)

In this way, the daily practice of very specific chiropractic techniques can be viewed as a form of martial art. Murphy has noted that martial arts can be used as a "many-sided, integral development of human nature." (1994, p. 448)

Fourth was his research into the holistic and energetic components of living humans. He determined that each vertebra was holistically linked to the health of the entire person, also that a vertebral subluxation at the first two cervical vertebra would cause systemic compensatory distortions throughout the spine and the body. He even examined how the electromagnetic nature of the physical organism was related to the environment and hence universal intelligence (Palmer, 1934, 1951a).

Put any one of these things together, and you may have a dramatic transformation for any individual. Put these together for B.J., who had already passed through the green-meme probably in the early 1950's, and you have the emergence of the yellow-meme and probably the turquoise-meme, and then perhaps coral, or the third tier.

B.J. Palmer's Buddhist Writings

I will not go so far as to say that Palmer was a Buddhist, because he never proclaimed this. From his writings and his Buddha statuette collection, it is obvious that he was greatly influenced by Buddhism and that in it he found a kindred philosophy and way of being (Palmer, 1949, 1950a, 1952, 1957).

In his 1953 text, *Upside Down and Right Side Up with B.J.*, he comments on the essence of Buddhism in Thailand mostly based on his study of Rhys Davids. Palmer wrote that Buddha taught, "middle path: impermanence of all things, and eventual complete dissolution of the being, escape thru Nirvana from all forms of sensation and consciousness which go to make life and suffering; and this by means of Four Great Truths, which a man must recognize before he sets out on his journey, and Eightfold Noble Path by which he will attain Nirvana." (1953, p. 694)

He really liked the teachings of Karma and Buddha's dismissal of the caste system as well as rituals, rites, and ceremonies. In this we can see aspects of Palmer's green-meme reaching out. Palmer wrote this after publishing several "green" books from 1949-1952, which had commentaries critiquing the formalism and ritual and ceremonies of Christianity.

He also liked that Buddhism did not focus on saving the soul but merging the consciousness with the basic goodness of the infinite. This was very close to his own quest to merge his consciousness with his innate intelligence and with the universal intelligence.

At the end of his essay on Buddhism, he comments on Havell's analysis of Buddha's death. Palmer wrote, "Buddha, having attained Maha Pari Nirvana at death, passing into boundless Ocean of Eternity, and reaching a state of Perfect Blessedness, free forever from sufferings of body and great illusion of senses, the Maha-Maya." (1953, p. 697) In this quote we can see that Palmer had a very clear understanding of Nirvana and the third tier.

After this book, he did not publish another book on philosophy until 1955. And then from 1957-1961, he completed six more books. In *Evolution or Revolution* he wrote,

"Yet INSIDE HIM is that greater INSIDE world he does not know, seldom recognizes, never fully understands. His limited finite understanding seeks to know the infinite unlimited world surrounding him, but fails dismally to realize that world he seeks is WITHIN HIM. Should that time come when his finite mind could and did KNOW the infinite mind WITHIN, then his external finite mind would cease to be, because it would then be infinite in scope, understanding, and application." (1958, p. 18)

In writings such as these, it becomes obvious that the Buddhist influence was substantial. And still, he considers Buddha, and all religions in general as manifestations of a certain time and certain place in a specific culture, so as to bring the individual closer to the infinite.

Palmer's Second Tier Analysis of Religion and Science

Palmer's insight into the role between religion and science represent the development of the yellow-meme or integrative consciousness. It is finally at this stage of development that the individual can reflect on the journey of development itself. This takes the ability of the systems perspective that everything is nested within everything else, that society itself has developed through stages.

Earlier we saw his unfavorable view of parts of India; here we see him not only embrace the development of rational thought, but discuss the

166

next step in development as the embrace from the educated brain of the innate within.

The present essay is focused on the individual's development, but these models are also used to examine the development of human culture over thousands of years (See Table 2). This ability to analyze the transformation of consciousness is a function of the second tier.

Palmer displayed this ability in his 1953 analysis of James Frazer's The Golden Bough, and again in his 1961 book, *The Great Divide*. Since we do not know for sure whether Palmer wrote the commentary to Frazer in 1953 or 1933 due to the rewriting of his manuscript, we are not sure when he achieved yellow integral consciousness. Table 3 is inferred based on his life and writings.

He has two critiques of Frazer, the first is that science is the handmaid of religion, not its antagonist. The second is that Buddhism is a dynamic religion. In both instances, he specified that science and religion have been at odds because religion is stuck in creeds and dogmas, and science does not accept the innate within all nature, a realization that comes if one looks inside.

Wilber has discussed a similar concept in regards to integral consciousness. That for science and religion to actually work together, then each must take a step towards the other. For example, science is to broaden its empiricism to include the study of subjective experience. Especially as to the practice of meditation and internal development. Spiritual traditions for millennia have tracked the progress of aspirants through a type of peer review from the elders. In this same regard, religion would need to accept as true only verifiable experience. Any stories or mythos that cannot as of yet be proven by scientific observation such as the virgin birth should be placed in brackets (1998). Both of these were advocated by Palmer in the early fifties.

The other concept that suggests that Palmer was an integral thinker is his notion of the Great Divide. He suggested that human consciousness was first split around 500 B.C., by Thales who helped humans to cultivate rationality and reason from their previous state of undifferentiated consciousness, and split the physical from the abstract, soul from body. The next step according to Palmer was to use this new conscious awareness, this educated intelligence to embrace the innate as the older and wiser source of all wisdom, and be guided by it. To him, this is what all of the great sages have done. To him the quickest

167

and most practical way for this abstract spiritual intelligence to be embraced by the educated thinking mind in the body is through the chiropractic adjustment.

Beck has noted that yellow-meme or integrative consciousness fully emerged on a wide scale for humans around 1950 (Roemischer, 2002). If this is true, then Palmer was on the cutting edge of his time. And, chiropractic may be the first healing art to be shaped by second tier thinking.

Holistic Integralism and Authentic Consciousness (Yellow-Turquoise)

The Authentic level of consciousness is one of the being levels. This is post formal development. Wilber calls this stage holistic integralism, and it encompasses Beck and Cowan's yellow and turquoise levels. It is difficult to distinguish exactly when Palmer entered the being levels. Perhaps it was after his trip to Cambodia. I hypothesize that he transformed vertically to the yellow-meme in 1953 upon re-writing his notes from his trip to South East Asia in 1933.

Wade's calls this the *authentic level*, where the self is no longer distorted by the ego. The mind and body become one. The person moves from egocentrism to humanocentrism. External validation is no longer needed. Here there is according to Wade, "A frank acknowledgement of the intuitive voice…accompanied by a cognitive sophistication far in advance of the 'gut' voice." (p. 163)

During this period, Palmer discusses his ability to listen to that "wee sma' voice." He even makes suggestions to others on how to get in touch with it. In fact, only the chiropractor that can listen to this voice, according to Palmer is truly practicing the art of chiropractic. "That special something," is required.

Palmer claimed that he started to listen to the innate wisdom as his guide for making decisions early on at age 17 (1949). He also discussed how he made his business decisions based on listening to the innate (1961c). He even carried a pad and pen with him at all times to write inspirations, especially at night by his bedside. He also suggested that

168

some chiropractors might take up yoga in order to attune to the infinite (1958).

Wade also describes the authentic consciousness as a point where the self as ego is pulled to the eternal ground of being. The person realizes that they construct their sense of self. Just as the ego matures, and the apex of the self's expression is achieved, the person becomes more open to letting go of the self altogether (1996). This level is also marked by systems and holistic thinking. I have discussed Palmer's use of systems thinking elsewhere (Senzon, 1999, 2000).

In the following quote, Palmer not only displays his authentic consciousness, but also reveals an insight into the levels above it.

Palmer wrote,

"This timeless, changeless order is an assurance of unchallenged authority; a sign of safe anchorage for the unsettled and undecided mind of man."

"Increase in man's knowledge does not mean the discovery of new things, but only his insight into his understanding of himself and his ability to use that which already is, always has been – like the growth of a child from infant to adult man, who digs deeper discovering worlds within man, new to him but old in time. When these are realized man can and will face uncertainty, secure in knowledge, at peace within himself, because he will be at peace with the Almighty law of the Universal as well as the Unital law within each created unit." (1961a, 176)

Like the growth of a child from infant to adult human he notes, development of universal awareness comes. This is a description of postformal development and third tier consciousness. The opening to the universal through the individual is coral-meme or transcendent development.

A four quadrant examination of Palmer's second tiered development can be started based mainly on his final writings (figure 4). In the lower left quadrant, he still continued to travel to Davenport for Lyceums (homecoming), and graduations, until his last year when his health would not allow travel. His final book, *Our Masterpiece*, is a historical chronicle of sorts, a cultural legacy. In the lower right quadrant would remain his final writings on philosophy, which have never been fully explored as a distinct period of the philosophy of chiropractic. In the upper right quadrant, there is not much of note. All of his attempts at scientific rational inquiry were complete. In his last works, he does write of the experiments and discusses what role they played in the evolution of chiropractic. In the upper left quadrant are, his second tier development, his illness, and any other development beyond that.

Upper Left Quadrant	Upper Right Quadrant
Yellow/Turquoise Holistic Integralism	• Discussions of research in Our Masterpiece.
Lower Left Quadrant	**Lower Right Quadrant**
• The conception of a Subluxation free world where all people know the innate within. • A call to action on many levels. • Lyceum and graduations. • Our Masterpiece volume 39.	1961: The Great Divide 1961: Law as applies to God and development 1957: Holistic/systems: Law of life and development 1950: 53: concepts of spiritual evolution of society 1949: theories of origin of innate, innate to innate communication 1936: holistic development of the concept of energy/body

Figure 4: Palmer's Tetra-Evolution; yellow/turquoise-meme.

Third Tier Transcendent Consciousness

The third tier is marked by three major levels of consciousness, Wilber classifies them as psychic, subtle, causal, or, nature mysticism, deity mysticism, and formless mysticism, and, prophet, saint, and sage. It is difficult to say whether Palmer fully embodied the third tier. Whether he did or not is up to interpretation. That he achieved holistic and integral consciousness is pretty clear. The third tier is more difficult to determine.

Wilber writes, "your individual I – your separate self or inner subject – becomes an object of the ultimate I, which is none other than radiant Spirit and your own true self. According to the mystics, you are one with God as ultimate Subject or pure Consciousness…" (2000, p. 34)

In *transcendent consciousness*, Wade suggests that the two aspects of awareness, one rooted in the body, the daily awareness, and the other rooted in the transcendent witness, the source of our truest self, merge. They become one. The truest self becomes part of daily awareness. One's value is then to merge with the infinite, the ground of being. The individual is then motivated to go beyond the self rooted in ego and grasp the eternal (1996).

To suggest that Palmer's last years were spent in transcendent consciousness, based only on his last few books, is a difficult stretch. While it does seem that he made an advance in his spiritual insights, these may have been heightened states of awareness and not necessarily established stages.

According to Cook-Greuter, the difference between postconventional development (second tier), and postpostconventional development (third tier), is vast. About the transcendent stage, she writes,

"The individual sees and experiences himself and others as part of ongoing humanity, embedded in the process of creation...Rational, waking consciousness is no longer perceived as a shackle but as just another phenomenon that assumes foreground or background status depending on the momentary focus." (1990, p. 93)

Does Palmer emphatically achieve this? We may never know. There are however, three aspects of Palmer's later writings that point towards an awakening into the third tier. The first is his use of the pronoun "We." The second is the completion of his quest, the highest answer yet, to his Chiropractic Zen-Koan. And the third is his finalistic teaching, his passing of the torch. I will deal with each of these separately.

Approaching the Third Tier as "We"

Palmer's use of the term "We" as opposed to "I" is the perfect place to start. In the early books, from 1906-1934, he went back and forth between the use of each pronoun. I liken this to getting used to a pair of shoes before finally committing to them and over time, they are broken in, and then eventually, the shoes become an extension of your foot. It is not until 1949, that he publicly announces the use of "we" and denounces the use of "I."

171

He wrote,

"This book, so far as the author is concerned, writes from the duality of personalities – the inseparable, indivisible, Siamese-twin personalities living in the one structure – the Innate and Educated individualities...To read this book and gain the viewpoint of its author, the reader must know the "we" or *he* will fail to gain the fundamental purpose of this book." (1949, foreword)

It is important to place this in context of his life. After years of study, examining thousands of skeletal remains, adjustments of thousands of patients, observing miraculous recoveries, traveling the world over, studying religions, losing loved ones, friends, making enemies, building an empire, and finally in 1948, he lost his wife Mabel. Sometime between 1938 and 1948, he "awoke." And from age 68 until his death at age 80, he wrote sixteen books totaling 8045 pages, and in each one, the pronoun used was "We." The consistency of his use of this pronoun not only in his writing, but also in his daily speech, points towards the dissolution of self and ego, and the acceptance of his self as a part of the universal.

If we study the conscious approach to his new pronoun through these twelve years, a glimmer of his process shines through. In all of the works from 1949-1953, he has a disclaimer in the foreword to the use of the term "We." The quote mentioned above is never repeated. In the six books between 1950-1952, he repeats the same foreword which notes that the use of "We" serves three purposes,

"1. It eliminates that disgusting and egotistical selfish pronoun "I" which constantly intrudes itself.
2. It permits the author to delineate his concept of the duality of personalities inhabiting one human home.
3. It broadly includes and spreads credit where credit is due, to any, every, and all people who have or are cooperating in building the structures, organizations, institutions, and associations which are an integral part of their lives." (1950, p. vii)

Obviously, this awareness came at the start of his green-meme, from 1949-1952. The above quote shows that his use of the term was anti hierarchical and egalitarian. From there, as he wrote and meditated on his new insights, he grew into second tier. This is noted by his foreword to his 1953 text; *Upside Down Inside Out*. In it, he notes that he went back through thousands of pages of notes form his trip in 1933,

172

and changed every pronoun. This was also the text that chronicles the Cambodian Buddhist ruins. I am suggesting that the very process of writing this book in 1953 was in part, a meditation on "We," and triggered Palmer to transform vertically into the second tier, from green to yellow.

After this, he does not mention the use of "We" again until 1961 the year of his death. In his book, *The Glory of Going On* (published posthumously by his son), he includes an entire chapter that recounts his awakening to the use of "We." The chapter itself is written almost as a sacred text. Many paragraphs begin with a variation of the capitalized words, "IT WAS IN THAT ONE ROOM," while intensely studying twenty thousand vertebra, night after night in his osteological lab. Much of the writings from this chapter sound represent the turquoise-meme, but certain statements, especially the one below, describe the coral-meme, or third tier. He wrote,

"IT WAS HERE IN THIS ONE ROOM, the Great Teacher and Master of ALL people of ALL times, was Innate. IT WAS HERE with these retired personalities, with the their every-day personal products, I learned the basic truths of Chiropractic and how to become a Chiropractor."

"Up till THIS period of MY life, I was INVOLVING MY thots, words, and acts much like so many have done and were doing. The "I" was egotistic as well as egoistic. After THIS period of OUR life, WE began EVOLVING like few people do or have done. From then on, WE thot, spoke, and acted. From then on, "I" was humble in the presence of Innate within as WE lived together."

"IT WAS THERE, plus time, IN THIS ONE ROOM, I found Myself WE found OURselves-INNATE AND I- until EACH lost his or her singular and single identity and became a plural duality, to eventually walk down the byways and highways together the rest of OUR lives." (1961a, p. 153)

I have discussed this topic elsewhere (Senzon, 2000), but not in such a linear fashion. This final writing on "We" shows not only an evolution of his conception of ego, but it also shows a clear movement towards the third tier.

Throughout Palmer's life, he had the incredible ability to master one level of consciousness, and develop the necessary skills for higher

173

ones. In the first two quotes above, and again in 1961, he uses the term duality when describing this shift in consciousness. Perhaps this experience was an altered state that touched the non-dual level of consciousness (a level above formless mysticism), where all duality between self and other disappears, and this moved Palmer so deeply that he changed the way in which he related to himself, his community, and the universe. He became "We," a "plural duality."

Zen Koan as Chiropractic Philosophy

From 1949-1955, he wrote much about the relationship between the individual and the infinite. For example, "Innate Intelligence is the Great I am that I am. Innate is the internal source of all and everything." (1955, p. 48) This was his exploration of the new consciousness. But then his writing changes, and from 1957-1961, these types of writings are geared more towards awakening to the internal God. And this becomes the answer that he always intimated, but never clearly expressed.

The answer to his lifelong question, "What is innate intelligence, and how does the chiropractic adjustment link it through the nervous system to the great universal intelligence?" finally arrives. To him God was the universal source of intelligence, which was behind all nature and the infinite ground. God as the infinite communicated to the finite through the innate intelligence. These writings lie between nature mysticism and non-dual mysticism, more as deity mysticism.

While Zen is focused on formless and nondual mysticism, Palmer's Koan brought him to deity mysticism, the subtle level of awareness, rather then the causal. His lifetime was spent immersed in seeking the experience of the psychic level, the nature mysticism, the innate intelligence which only exists in living forms. This led him to the level above it. His understanding of the subtle level of consciousness, the deity mysticism is evidenced by the following quote.

Palmer writes,

"Every Chiropractor, whether he realizes it or not, every time he corrects the impediment between the living "GOD" in man, IS AN APOSTLE of that living "God," bringing into reality the Living Intellectual "God" from above, permitting it to work thru the living material bodies of all mankind. IT IS A LIVING PROVABLE "GOD"

174

IN MAN, THE VERY SOUL AND LAW OF HIS BEING." (1961a, p. 261)

And thus, as an extension of his insight into the role of the freed innate wisdom for man to unify with, chiropractic became for him a practical means to answer the questions of all religions while healing people in the meantime. To Palmer, the philosophy of chiropractic is rooted in a mind/body/spirit triune that is only real for the soul that chooses to pursue the truth of it in their daily experience.

The Call as Bodhisattva Challenge

Beginning in the late 1950's, Palmer's mortality was evident. He wrote more and more to the future, to those who would carry on his and his father's legacy. The truth of his very existence was the expression of the universe through the individual by way of the chiropractic adjustment. He did not have faith or belief, only experience. And this, he sought desperately to pass on. An example of this call, this challenge from the third tier to the first and second tiers, was as follows,

"Time ALWAYS has and ALWAYS WILL perpetuate those methods which better serve mankind."
"CHIROPRACTIC IS NO EXCEPTION TO THAT RULE."
"Our illustrious father placed this Chiropractic trust in OUR keeping, to keep it pure and not sullied or defamed. We pass it on to you unstained, to protect as he would also have you do."
"As he passed on, so will we. We admonish you to keep this principle and practice unadulterated and unmixed. Humanity needed THEN what he gave us. You need what we NOW give you. Out there in those great open spaces are multitudes seeking what YOU possess."
"The burdens are heavy; responsibilities are many; obligations are providential; but the satisfaction of traveling the populated highways and byways relieving suffering, prolonging lives, adding millions of years to lives of millions of suffering people, will bring forth satisfactions and glories with greater blessings than you think."
"Time is of the essence."
"May God flow from ABOVE-DOWN His bounteous strengths, courages, and understandings to carry on; and may your Innates receive and act on that free flow of wisdom from ABOVE-DOWN, INSIDE-OUT; for you HAVE in YOUR possession a sacred trust. Guard it well." (1961a, p. 253)

175

In the last years of his life, from 1948-1961, when Palmer was achieving these new structures of consciousness and tirelessly writing sixteen volumes, his body failed him. Plagued by ulcers and other forms of GI disturbances, eventually he was diagnosed with a malignant tumor of the bowel (Quigley, 1989). B.J. Palmer died on May 27, 1961. A life of genuine search for the ultimate answers was completed.

Conclusion

By understanding B.J. Palmer as an advanced soul that lived on the cutting edge of the cultural evolution of the last century, chiropractic as a health and wellness discipline can be viewed in a new light. In his later years, Palmer derided any chiropractors that were based in the blue or orange and even green-memes.

He wanted chiropractic to be an integral approach to health, but not in the sense of integral medicine, where alternative methods and therapies were used to treat an illness. His perspective was much broader than that. He thought that by adjusting the spine and removing the impediment to the flow of intelligent energy in the body, that the individual would get healthier and more in tune with their inner most nature. Thus, body, heart, mind, soul, and spirit could all be transformed by the chiropractic adjustment.

His vision was global. He thought far into the future and wanted to bring a new spiritual and practical truth to humanity. Chiropractic as a unique discipline then, stands far out from the field of medicine. And, in the chiropractic of today, there is great disparity as to practice, philosophy and intent. Although, most chiropractors do seek to allow for the innate intelligence to become manifest as health, very few see their role as spiritual guide to the infinite source. This is what Palmer, and his father before him envisioned.

References

Astin, J., Astin, W. (2001). "An integral approach to medicine."
    Alternative Therapies in Health and Medicine, 8(2): 70-75.
Beck, D., Cowan, C. (1996). Spiral dynamics: Mastering values,
    leadership, and change. Oxford: Blackwell Publishers.
Chia, M., Winn, M. (1984). Taoist secrets of love: Cultivating male
    sexual energy. Sante Fe: Aurora Press.
Cook-Greuter, S. (1990). "Maps for living: Ego-development stages
    from symbiosis to conscious universal embeddedness."
    [Chapter]. Commons, M., Armon, C. Kohlberg, L., Richards,
    F., Grotzner, T., Sinnott, J. (eds.) (1990). Adult development;
    volume 2: Models and Methods in the study o fadolescent and
    adult thought. New York: Praeger.
Cook-Greuter, S. (1999). Postautonomous ego development: A study of
    its nature and measurement. [Dissertation]. Ann Arbor: UMI.
Combs, A. (1995/2002). The radiance of being: Understanding the
    grand integral vision; living the integral life. Second edition.
    St. Paul: Paragon House.
Deida, D. (1997). The way of the superior man: A spiritual guide to
    mastering the challenges of women work and sexual desire.
    Austin: Plexus.
Dye, A. (1939). The evolution of chiropractic: It's discovery and
    development. Philadelphia: A. E. Dye.
Gaucher, P.L. (1993). Chiropractic: Early concepts in their historical
    setting. Chicago: National College of Chiropractic.
Gibbons, R.W. (1987). "Assessing the oracle at the Fountainhead: B.J.
    Palmer and his times, 1902-1961." Chiropractic History,
    7(1):8-14.
Gielow, V. (1981). Old dad chiro: A biography of D.D. Palmer founder
    of chiropractic. La Crosse, WI: Fred H. Barge.
Ginsburg, H. Opper, S. (1969). Piaget's theory of intellectual
    development. Englewood Cliffs, NJ: Prentice Hall.
Holmes, A.T. (1924). Malpractice as applied to chiropractors; vol. 17.
    Davenport: Palmer College.
Keating, J. (1997). B.J. of Davenport: The early years of chiropractic.
    Davenport, Iowa: Association for the History of Chiropractic.
Loevinger, J. (1976). Ego development: Conceptions and theories. San
    Francisco: Jossey Bass.

Maynard, J.E. (1959/1982). Healing hands: The story of the Palmer family discoverers and developers of chiropractic. Revised edition. MS: Jonorm Publishers.

Murphy M. (1994). The future of the body: Explorations into the further evolution of human nature. Los Angeles: Tarcher.

Palmer, B.J. (1908/1911). The philosophy and principles of chiropractic adjustments: A series of thirty eight lectures; vol. 3. Davenport, IA: Palmer College.

_____. (1920). A textbook on the Palmer technique of chiropractic; vol. 13. Davenport, IA: Palmer College.

_____. (1926). 'Round the world with B.J. Palmer. Davenport, IA: Palmer College.

_____. (1934). The Subluxation specific the adjustment specific Davenport, IA: Palmer College.

_____. (1936). The known man or an explanation of the "phenomenon of life"; vol. 19. Davenport, IA: Palmer College.

_____. (1949). The Bigness of the Fellow Within; vol. 22. Davenport, IA: Palmer College.

_____. (1950a). Up from below the bottom; vol. 23. Palmer College, Davenport, IA.

_____. (1950b). Fight to climb; vol. 24. Davenport, IA: Palmer College.

_____. (1951a). Clinical controlled chiropractic research; vol. 25. Davenport, IA: Palmer College.

_____. (1951b). Conflicts Clarify; vol. 26. Davenport, IA: Palmer College.

_____. (1951c). History Repeats; vol. 27. Davenport, IA: Palmer College

_____. (1952). Answers; vol. 28. Davenport, IA: Palmer College.

_____. (1953). Upside down inside out with B.J.; vol. 29. Davenport, IA: Palmer College.

_____. (1955). Fame and Fortune; vol. 33. Davenport, IA: Palmer College.

_____. (1957). Evolution or Revolution; vol. 34. Davenport, IA: Palmer College.

_____. (1958). Palmer's law of life; vol. 36. Davenport, IA: Palmer College.

_____. (1961a). The Glory of Going On; vol. 37. Davenport, IA: Palmer College.

_____. (1961b). The Great Divide; vol. 38. Davenport, IA: Palmer College.

_____. (1961c). Our Masterpiece; vol. 39. Davenport, IA: Palmer College.

Palmer, D.D. (1910). The chiropractor's adjuster. Portland: Portland Printing Company.

Palmer, David. (1967). Three generations; The history of chiropractic. Palmer College of Chiropractic. Davenport.

Peterson, D., Weiss, G. (1995). Chiropractic; An illustrated history. St. Louis: Mosby.

Quigley, H. (1989). "The last days of B.J. Palmer: Revolutionary confronts reality." Chiropractic History. 9;2: 11-19.

Reid. D. (1989). The Tao of health, sex, & longevity: A modern practical guide to the ancient way. New York: Fireside.

Rehm, W.S., (1986). "Legally defensible: Chiropractic in the courtroom and after, 1907." Chiropractic History. 6: 51-55.

Roemischer, J. (2002). "The never-ending upward quest; A WIE editor encounters the practical and spiritual wisdom of spiral dynamics; An interview with Dr. Don Beck. What is Enlightenment, Fall/Winter, 105-126.

Senzon, S.A. (1999). "Causation as related to self organization and health related quality of life expression based on the vertebral subluxation model, the philosophy of chiropractic and the new biology." Journal of Vertebral Subluxation Research, 3;4: 104-112.

Senzon, S.A. (2000). "An integral approach to the philosophy of chiropractic: B.J. Palmer's model of consciousness." Journal of Integral Studies, volume 1.

Sinnott, R. (1997). The Green Books; A collection of timeless Chiropractic works – by those who lived it! Mokena, IL: Chiropractic Books.

Wade, J. (1996). Changes of mind; A holonomic theory of the evolution of consciousness. SUNY Press, Albany.

Wardwell, W. (1992). Chiropractic: History and evolution of a new profession. St. Louis: Mosby.

Washburn, M. (1988). The ego and the dynamic ground. Albany: SUNY Press.

Weise, G., Lykins, W.R. (1986). "A bibliography of the Palmer Green Books in Print, 1906-1985," Chiropractic History, 6(1):64-74.

Wilber, K. (1986). "The spectrum of psychopathology." In Wilber, K. Engler, J. and Brown, D. (1986). Transformations of consciousness; Conventional and contemplative perspectives on development. Boston: New Science Library.

_____. (1995). Sex ecology and spirituality; The spirit of evolution. Boston: Shambhala.

_____. (1997). The eye of spirit; An integral vision for a world gone slightly mad. Boston: Shambhala.

_____. (1998). The marriage of sense and soul; Integrating science and religion. Boston: Shambhala.

_____. (1999). "Boomeritis vs. spiritual growth in the new millennium." Tikkun, vol 14, issue 6, 1999.

_____. (2000). Integral Psychology; Consciousness, Spirit, Psychology, Therapy. Boston: Shambhala.

_____. (2001). "On Critics, Integral Institute, My Recent Writing, and Other Matters of Little Consequence: A Shambhala Interview with Ken Wilber part II." http://wilber.shambhala.com/html/interviews/interview1220_2.cfm/).